TALES FROM THE BLUE STACKS

TALES FROM THE
BLUE STACKS.

ROBERT BERNEN

CHARLES SCRIBNER'S SONS
NEW YORK

Copyright © 1978 Robert Bernen

Library of Congress Cataloging in Publication Data

Bernen, Robert.
    Tales from the Blue Stacks.
    1. Blue Stack Mountains, Ire.—Fiction. I. Title.
PZ4.B52454Tal   1978   [PR6052.E64]   941.6'93
78-3742
ISBN 0-684-15540-0

1 3 5 7 9 11 13 15 17 19 H/C 20 18 16 14 12 10 8 6 4 2

Printed in the United States of America

CONTENTS

FOREWORD

Ten miles north of Donegal Town, in the extreme north-west of Ireland, runs a range of low, rounded hills known as the Blue Stacks. Technically, they are classed as mountains, but to the ordinary eye they look like hills. Their name—taken from the Irish name of the highest peak, Croagh Gorm—is fitting, for from a distance they always appear a deep, purple blue, even on the clearest days. Around these hills lives a small group of farmers whose lives continue to be rooted in eighteenth-century patterns, or earlier. Technologically and agriculturally their methods scarcely reveal modern influence. Tools we read about in histories of ancient and medieval technology can still be seen in use on Blue Stack farms, some of them home-made in forms that have long since disappeared elsewhere. Machines are seldom heard.

Though these old traditions are now rapidly fading, as the last generation of Irish-speaking farmers dies out and young, English-speaking literate ones take their place, something still remains, both in the crafts of life and in its thought-patterns. Habits of thrift and personal independence have kept men as far outside a money-based economy as possible, so that even the houses are often still made from materials found within the boundaries of each farm—unshaped stone, rough wooden rafters, green-thatch rooves. Crops of potatoes and corn are still sown and reaped entirely with spade and scythe; hay is mown by hand; fuel is won from the surrounding bog by laborious hand-cutting and sun-drying. As interesting, however, as the ways of life are the forms of thought that accompany them, especially in an age that is so rapidly sweeping away all living remnants of its own long past.

Into this bit of anachronous farming community a modern man and his wife moved, to farm sheep and to live in the manner of their neighbours. Some of what they heard, saw, or themselves experienced is recorded in the following tales. The tales are therefore unlike fiction, which falsifies in order to achieve a greater effect. The aim here has been to preserve a true picture of some aspects of Blue Stack life at the moment of its final disappearance, and as it fades into the modern world around it.

Marauder

One morning in the years before there was an Irish republic, Peadar Kennedy stepped out of his whitewashed stone thatched house on the side of a rough and heathery hill. The summer sun was already high in an almost cloudless sky, even though by the clock it was only 6 a.m., and Peadar, just out of bed, had not yet put in his teeth and his pink gums showed brightly as he yawned and ran his hand over his still disorganized grey hair. He had put on his black tweed trousers but not his flannel shirt, so that his ragged suspenders rested on the shoulders of the yellowed woollen undershirt he never went without every day of the year, winter and summer, and the very top of his thin but sinewy and powerful torso and neck could be seen where the opening of the undershirt left a wide space of chest and shoulder bare. That space was a smooth, almost sickly white by contrast with the rough texture of his neck and face, coloured less by the sun, which was rarely seen in those hills, than by the wind that blew almost continually, perhaps even by the spitting rains.

On this morning there was no sign of rain. It looked like the best spell of the summer coming on and—it was late July— Peadar thought it might be wise to cut a section of the 'park', as he called his meadow, and take advantage of the almost sure spell of dry days ahead. His eyes ran along the meadow grass from its lowest point near the small swift stream two hundred yards below him and so, carefully speculating about the condition of the grass, slowly upwards to the fence above the house that kept the sheep on the mountain and out of the fine inland grass saved for hay. Then his eyes paused and then moved more quickly upwards along the rough, boggy heather of the hill. His face fell into a position of complete relaxation that in him indicated the same onset of concentration that would be marked in a city man by a gesture the exact opposite, a drawing together of the features to mirror the inner intensity of effort. If anything at all indicated that Peadar's mind was occupied with a problem, it was only that his small, narrow eyes were a shade wider open than they had been and his erect body and his hands were very still. He remained in that attitude for less than a minute, then turned without visible preoccupation and went back into the house, where his sister had rekindled the fire from the turf coals that had been buried in their own ashes the night before and on which the kettle was beginning to steam.

Peadar now set about shaving, an operation he never omitted even on the busiest of harvest days, and thought of getting his tea. His sister would make her own tea but not his. It was not a matter of enmity, just habit. They always ate separately, Peadar at the table, his sister rocking herself forward and back on a low stool by the hearth. As he sat down to his cup of tea this morning Peadar saw the early sun shine off the feathers of the hens pecking before the house and he thought again of the meadow and of the new scythe he had bought the week before.

'It looks to be a good one,' he murmured to himself.

Then he remembered that something had caught his attention as he had looked at the steep hill above the meadow ground. Or, more accurately, the absence of something. For at that hour he would expect to find a number of his sheep not far above the meadow fence, where he had seen them settle down for the night not many hours before. They could have moved over the hill to the far side in the early light before he had risen, but with the wind from the east, blowing directly on to the face of the hill, they would suffer less from early midges on the near side of the hill. The complete absence of sheep was odd enough to make him decide to put off all other work until he had gone out to look over his flock.

When Peadar had finished his tea and bread he crossed himself rapidly, put on his tweed cap, pulled a charred briar pipe, the last inch of mouthpiece broken away, from one pocket and from another a pen-knife with one polished worn blade and a plug of hard, dark tobacco, from which he began cutting rough chunks. These chunks he rubbed against the base of his palm, stuffed the pipe, and lit it with a coal from the fire held in an old pair of iron tongs. Then he spat into the fire and sat so, smoking and looking at the fire, spitting at intervals, saying nothing to his sister and not apparently absorbed in thoughts of any importance. In fact he was not much concerned about the absence of the sheep, for anything could have put them over the hill—too many midges or a stray dog wandering by, perhaps. At any rate, he would soon have a look at them.

His old briar pipe produced a thin whistling sound, so hard did he draw on it to keep the rough tobacco lit, and when he put another coal to it and drew rapidly with his breath the moisture in the bottom of the pipe bowl gurgled noisily. Finally he got up, put his chair back to the wall away from the fire, and went out. At the far end of the house was a small shed, not more than four feet high, of rough stone without mortar and with a slanting roof of rusting corrugated iron sheets. He loosened the bit of wire that held the crude wooden door shut and spoke softly to his dog.

'Poor Fly, poor Fly, come out now and take your tea!'

When Peadar had fed the dog a breakfast like his own of tea and bread, the two set off together up the hill. He knew he could be away until nightfall if he wished, for his sister would attend to the cows and the hens and bring in a heavy creel of turf as well as he could himself. It was not so in the past. For years, before his sister returned from domestic service in the town, he had lived there alone and had done all the work of the farm and all the chores of the household himself, everything from the heavy labour of dipping sheep to the feminine tasks of washing and mending. 'I have no one, on'y myself,' he would say when the matter came into conversation. The hardest part of it in those days was that he could never leave the farm for more than twelve hours. The cows had to be milked regularly and the hens closed in securely at night, safe from the badgers and foxes that often stole down in the heavy mists of the long summer evenings. In winter the animals had to be foddered and watered. And even after only a few hours away from the house the fire would be out when he returned. Now his sister saw to all that and he often spent whole days on the hill, returning only by the last fading light or even, when there was a moon, well after sunset. Yet he would not have been afraid to be caught by darkness, as he often was by the heavy mountain mist, for he was sure he knew every yard of the ground by heart.

As Peadar slowly climbed the hill now, a heavy ash-plant stick in his left hand and his dog near him, trotting ahead and then turning and waiting for him, his mind went back to the problem that had presented itself earlier, the absence of the sheep. He did not think there had been midges out that morning to chase them over the hill, but the rough grass on the moorland over the crest of the hill was sweet at that time of the year, especially after a clear night when it had been touched by a light summer frost. He would see them soon, he thought to himself. He was near the crest of the hill and paused to look around.

About two hundred yards distant, near a low sod dike that divided his land from his neighbour's, he caught sight of a ewe. She was standing beside an overhanging bank of turf, and that had kept him from seeing her sooner. Instantly, even before he could think the words, he knew that the ewe was 'not right'. She was standing quite still, facing the bank of turf, neither grazing nor moving her jaws as she would be doing if she were chewing the cud. Peadar began walking towards her slowly. She was a four year old ewe, a good

4

rearer of lambs, with plenty of milk, and this year she had a strong ewe-lamb with her, born early, in the middle of April. He was still well distant when he saw the ewe shift slightly— she had noticed him coming—and now he saw that she was standing stiff-legged, with her right foreleg set slightly but awkwardly forward.

Peadar's mind leapt swiftly ahead reconstructing the night's events. Something had happened to the flock, that was clear. He would know the whole story as soon as he got to the ewe. He hurried his step but his dog, as if in confirmation of his intuitions, suddenly fell back and, moving backwards and forwards over a short path several times, settled down into the rough grass and refused to follow. Only as Peadar came up to the ewe did he see the lamb close in to the bank, lying on its right side, its legs stiffly out before it, the left foreleg slightly raised in the air. Apart from the stiffness it could have been sleeping. There was no sign of injury. The ewe backed off a few steps and stamped one forepaw into the ground. It was meant to be threatening but only had an effect of petulance. Peadar contemplated the scene for a moment without moving. Then he turned away and looked again over as much of the hill as he could see and far down into the valley below. Slanting lines of smoke were rising above the thatched rooves of the whitewashed stone houses. On one farm two children, a boy and a girl, were chasing the cows home to be milked. On another the hens were being fed. His eye rested on every flock of sheep, and all were grazing normally, without any sign of trouble. He looked over his neighbour's land carefully and back over as much of his own as he could see, searching for another sign or hint, but found none. Then he went back to the lamb. Bending over from the waist, he put his hand to the lamb's neck just under the ear and separated the wool. Two small black holes confirmed his thought: it had been a dog, a dog that killed alone and, unlike those that sometimes ran out in pairs or small gangs, this dog did not kill for sport, but for blood.

'I knew then that the one that did it would be back again,'

Peadar said when he was telling the story later. 'A dog that kills to suck the blood is not like another that tears the sheep and leaves them. That one will go out in twoses and threeses, and always to another place, but this un'll go always alone. Isn't it great too how he left all others and picked on'y my sheep?'

All in all he found four dead lambs that first morning, each with two holes in the neck and the blood sucked out. He judged from their condition that they were not long dead. The dog had come sometime in the morning. Over the hill his sheep had moved far off from the house, off westwards, and were huddling in clusters in close to banks of turf or large overhanging rocks. Two ewes were lame, but none showed signs of having been caught by the dog. Some were not grazing even yet, and some of the ewes had been separated from their lambs. Peadar spent the rest of the day going over the whole of his land, and beyond it into the neighbouring hills if he expected to find any of his sheep there. It soon became clear to him that only the sheep near in to the house had been selected. The distant ones were still grazing quietly, looking up and bleating to their lambs as they became aware of Peadar's approach, the lambs themselves running swiftly over to their mothers and sucking anxiously for milk. The larger lambs were big now to the point where they had to bend their forelegs and go down on to the joints to get their mouths under the ewe. Then, as the ewe felt the lamb get its first suck and establish identity, she would walk a few steps off, pause to let the lamb fall in behind her, and then move off again. But Peadar stayed as far from them as he could, and kept his dog in close to his heels. He had no desire to disturb the sheep. By late afternoon he had seen all his sheep and had made sure that the separated ewes and lambs had come together again. Then he went down to the house, got a spade, went back up the hill, and buried the four dead lambs. Other farmers, he knew, would have put poison down near, or in, the dead lambs, leaving their bodies where they were, hoping the killer

6

would return to them. But he himself never used poison. He had seen birds lift it and drop it in other places, sometimes near houses, and good dogs had got it and been killed that way. Besides, he was sure that when this dog returned—and he knew it would—it would go for live sheep only.

When he returned to the house, he found that his sister had set out on the table a plate of potatoes that had been boiled and ready hours before, and which she had kept warm in a large round-bellied iron pot by the side of the hearth. A pitcher of milk stood on the table and a small salt-cellar. Peadar ate the potatoes in silence, taking large, slow mouthfuls. When he was finished he boiled a small tin pot of tea over a few coals raked to the centre of the hearth and then he repeated the morning's routine with pipe, knife and tobacco, and sat there thus, smoking, spitting into the fire, and from time to time relighting the pipe with a bit of twisted paper made into a torch, the wrapping of some parcel of food brought from the town, ignited at the hearth. His sister sat to one side and slightly behind him, as always, but not rocking now as she usually did. She sat still, her wrinkled hands out flat, palms down on the sooty apron and soiled dress that covered her legs to well below the knees, waiting, Peadar knew, for him to tell what had happened. They seldom talked, but she had watched him take the spade into the hills, and had been waiting outside when he returned. He knew that the reason she was sitting so still was because she was waiting for him to speak.

'That dog come a long way,' she said in a high, thin, singing voice—she was over seventy and her native Irish had left a strong mark too on her way of speaking—when he had finished telling her about the sheep. 'Did I not tell you the other day, watch the sheep?'

His sister often claimed 'foreknowledge' of events. It was true, he remembered, she had said something to him two or three days earlier about the sheep, and he had seen her the day before looking towards the hill. But she said many things, as often wrong as right, and he had learned not to pay too much attention to her warnings.

That night Peadar tied his dog to his own bed and put down an old sack for her to sleep on. It was, for the moment, unnecessary, he thought. The killer dog was not likely to return so soon. But when it did there was a chance his own dog would let him know. That night his sleep was not disturbed, nor for several nights afterwards. Then he began sleeping less soundly, waking from time to time and listening, in the total stillness of the summer night around his house, for some stirring or some restlessness of his dog under his bed. One night, about a week after the loss of the lambs, he rose in the middle of the night and went out. An almost full moon showed him the sheep resting or grazing quietly on the hill. Finally, when two weeks had gone by, he thought it was time for the dog to return, if it was going to, and when he saw his sister looking for a long while at the hill that morning, he knew her thought was like his own. Now he began to stir more in the middle of the night, but still no dog came. Another week passed, and he awoke one night in the darkness to a sound, something between sniffling and whimpering, from his own dog underneath the bed. He lay still and listened. The dog had dreams sometimes and gave out little stifled barks and whimpers, as if she were fighting, or gathering in unwilling sheep in her sleep. This time, the dog was awake.

'Hush, you Fly!' Peadar whispered and got out of bed. Quickly pulling on his trousers, he went to the door and out in his bare feet on to the broad flagstones that paved the area before the door. A sliver of moon gave a pale light, and he could see the sheep moving rapidly in a flock, with the faint, almost not visible form of a dog moving swiftly, agilely, around them. They were heading up the hill.

Peadar went back into the house, pulled his flannel shirt over his head, adjusted his suspenders and pulled on a red, home-knitted pullover. He touched his sister's shoulder to wake her, but she was already awake, and turned her head slightly.

8

'When you have the fire made, take Fly and see about the sheep,' he said.

Then, taking his jacket from a wall-peg and putting his cap on his head, he told his dog to lie down, and went out.

His problem was to get the killer dog away from the sheep quickly, before it could do any harm, but alarming it as little as possible. He meant to follow the dog to its home if he could and claim the price of his dead sheep. He was barefooted, as often at that time of the year, and could move faster than with boots. Still, it was not easy following a dog. A dog, he knew, could travel eight or ten miles in a night, and could always outpace a man. And he was not a good runner. He had never been fast on his feet. He went everywhere at a steady walk. Luck would have to be with him if he was to follow this dog all the way. But he also knew that the dog would probably take a roundabout route home, especially when followed, and he had a chance of gaining on him then, for he knew dogs and their ways.

These thoughts had been gone over many times before and now as he hurried up the hill, over the fence that divided hill from meadow, over the burn, past his stacks of thatched turf, all that was in his mind was to reach the sheep before the dog had actually closed in on them. He kept westward as he moved upwards, going towards a place where the dog could push the sheep against overhanging banks of turf and hem them in. But as he crossed the smooth rounded crest of the hill, and a vast flat basin of marshy land and stiff red grass, grey then in the pale moonlight, opened before him, he saw he had been wrong. The dog had not pushed the sheep back to the steep banks of rock and turf. Instead he had them in a tight group and was moving them around—not fast, but attentively, alert, setting them moving, lunging towards them, working them, confusing them, waiting for the moment when he would close in on the first straggler. Peadar thought he still had time, that no sheep had yet been killed. He watched the scene for only a part of a moment, then he whistled softly, a low short easy whistle, not very loud. The sheep lifted their

9

heads abruptly in the direction of the sound but the dog did not at once notice the noise, so absorbed was he in his prey. Again Peadar whistled, low and soft as before, with nothing menacing about it. Now the dog stopped and looked about. As Peadar began moving towards the sheep the dog retired.

'Good pup, good pup,' Peadar called quietly.

The dog raised his head and put his ears up, then he turned and moved back a few yards, stopped again and watched Peadar. For a moment he was plainly uncertain and wavered. His instinct told him to flee but he was confused. Peadar's voice had something in it that attracted him, that made him trust the man.

'Good pup,' Peadar said again softly. 'Come here, pup. Come here.'

The dog looked on, puzzled. It was a large brown dog with white markings. There were many dogs like it in the hills, but this one was larger than almost any Peadar had seen before. He was a young dog and his fine coat and high condition showed that he had a good home. His dark eyes glinted brightly, then narrowed as Peadar watched him, and seemed to slant very slightly like those of a fox. The dog's lower jaw fell, leaving the mouth just barely open, the teeth just visible, anticipatory.

'Come here, pup,' Peadar called again.

But the dog had made its decision: the man was his enemy, not to be trusted. He turned and started away, head and tail down. Peadar thought he had got his first hint as he saw the dog start away to the southeast, not moving directly away from him but obliquely. He wondered if that was the direction of its home. Then the dog changed his direction suddenly and started away to the north. To the north there were three miles of flat marshy land. If the dog went that way Peadar could keep him in sight until he reached the other bank of hills. But what then? The dog would dash across the hills and away before he could come up with it. But if it were only a feint on the dog's part, so much the better having him in sight.

So began the chase. The swift, young, vicious animal that had been the hunter now became the hunted, fleeing from the slow and plodding but ominous dark figure of the man, who was armed against the speed and cunning of the dog with only his years of experience of training and using and watching sheep dogs. The contest was not as unequal as it seemed. Peadar, seeing that the dog was afraid of him—of all men, probably—thought that sooner or later that would give him an advantage.

The dog was not easy to keep sight of in the rough, reddish boggy land. At times all that gave him away was the bright white fur at the end of his full, furry tail. Peadar followed his first thought as to the direction of the dog's home and kept to the south. The dog moved along in a more or less parallel direction to him, going eastwards but always remaining to the north, moving slowly, indirectly, lying down at times, at others reversing his course and going back in the other direction. In general he moved eastwards and Peadar's first guess seemed right. The two reached the high hills to the east at almost the same time. Peadar knew the dog had two ways he could go then. To the northeast beyond the hills was a glen of small farmers who kept mostly sheep and only a few cattle, to the south a broader valley of cattle and dairy farms. If the dog went to the north Peadar knew he could easily find him among the houses there, all of them poor hill farms like his own, the farmers well-known to him. As he lost sight of the dog entering the hills he headed for a knoll that would give him a view of the valley below to the south, a valley of well-drained clay land, an area of cattle more than sheep, of good crops of oats, barley, potatoes and carrots. He had few acquaintances there, and little reason to go there.

He had lost sight of the dog in the hills but he had reached the knoll, with a chance of locating him again. The sun had risen. The valley was below him. He sat down on a tuft of dry heather and dug out his pipe and tobacco and knife. He could easily lose the dog for good now, he knew. He must follow it right to its home or he could do nothing about it even if he found it again later. As he smoked he wondered what chance he would have of getting the price of his dead lambs. Men who could read and write had ways of doing things he knew nothing about. After a while he saw the dog again, below him, possibly half a mile away. He started after it and could see that it was still following a broken path, not going directly towards its home. At times it would stop under a low tree or a hedge and lie down. Then Peadar would loiter too, but always trying to keep the dog in sight. Once out of the hills, on the flatter land below, things became more difficult again. There was a road to follow here, but there were side roads too, trees and hedges, houses, barns and ditches. The dog knew this ground and Peadar did not. Two or three times he lost sight of the brown fur so long he thought the dog had got away from him. Then he would stop and look over the landscape patiently, his unshaven, grey-bristled face in that same relaxed attitude it always assumed when a problem presented itself to him. His eyes moved steadily from field to field, without haste, taking in no specific object, receptive to general impressions. Here all was green. There was no heather and rushes were sparse. Most of the hay had been cut and won and put up in cocks, and a soft light green aftergrass had sprung from the ground around them. The houses were large and prosperous looking, with outbuildings and, in some cases, tall round-roofed hay sheds. Fields of dark earth with yellow stalks of stubble indicated where barley or oats had stood and recently been cut. Cattle were grazing quietly. The morning was still early. Peadar was now six miles or so from his own farm, but no one here was yet up.

So by irregular starts and stops he followed the dog to a spot near a two-storey house with a fine slate roof, well kept. This was a house Peadar knew. The owner kept a large herd of cattle, which were grazing then in surrounding pastures. Peadar had seen him at marts, though they had never spoken. He seldom took a drink, Peadar knew, and was famous for his tenacity in getting the price he wanted for his animals. Peadar had never had any dealings with him.

The dog had been lurking at the hedge that separated two farms. Peadar watched him now as he moved forward from the hedge to a small tin-roofed shed built on to the byre. As he neared the shed the dog moved more swiftly until with a sudden leap he rose and disappeared through a small window on the side of one wall. The dog had reached home.

When he had seen the dog go into the shed, Peadar saw no reason to hesitate, but went straight to the door of the two-storey house and knocked loudly. A long while passed without any answer. Again he knocked, and a third time. Finally the door opened and a heavy woman with matted dark hair that hung around a long, angular face broken into many flat planes, and half-open eyes that showed only a suggestion of alarm behind their sleepiness, looked out. She was still in her night-dress, an old raincoat over it, her feet in well-worn cloth slippers. She eyed Peadar blankly, her look of curiosity, ready to receive some unknown alarm, changing rapidly to one of defensive but repressed indignation. She had never seen this man before and her first reaction was mistrust.

She did not put her question in words, but stared steadily at Peadar, and her hand shifted slightly sideways to let him know he should speak.

'Is himself at home?'

'Himself? What do you want?'

Peadar told her who he was, but would not tell his business. The woman closed the door and Peadar waited. After about a quarter of an hour a large man—Peadar's 'himself'—opened the door and stepped out. Peadar identified himself again and the other nodded acquiescence, as if to acknowledge having seen him at the marts and being generally aware of who he was. He had not said a word, but his manner invited Peadar to continue, and while Peadar told him briskly about the killings his face kept its same not unfriendly look. Only when Peadar had finished did a darkness come over the large man's face in reaction to the new and unwelcome problem in his life at a busy time of the year. Then, looking at Peadar for a moment, he finally spoke.

'That dog's tied at nightfall.' And, without saying any more, he led the way to the shed Peadar had seen the dog enter. He was only a few years younger than Peadar, but tall and heavy, and his thick, large hands reminded Peadar that he had heard it said that this man had milked thirty cows every morning and evening when he was young. Stopping at the door of the shed he looked at Peadar steadily, curiously, but his face was not set in a frown. Rather there was something almost like a smile about his tightly closed lips.

When the two men entered the shed the dog, lying asleep, stirred and turned its head. Before it lay a chipped enamel wash-bowl with bits of dried food sticking to the edges. The dog rose slowly and stretched, then put its nose into the bowl and licked the edges. At that moment Peadar noticed the chain.

The large man looked at him without speaking. The dog was chained; the chain, leading from a large stone to a leather collar around the dog's neck, was only about eighteen inches long.

'That's the dog was after my sheep today,' Peadar said.

The other bent down to release the snap on the dog's collar and, straightening again, said, 'Come in for tea. You have a good way to go.'

*

Pondering the event later, Peadar had no doubt that he had the right dog. There was no mystery about the way he had come to be chained. Peadar had often seen young pups working away at their collars until they learned to slip their heads out. Some of the cleverest of them would learn to put their heads back in again. But there was nothing he could do about the dog. The question remained: would it come back again? He was certain it had its freedom every night, since the collar could not hold it.

He kept his own dog tied by his bed at night. Three weeks more passed without a sign of the killer dog. The meadow had been cut, swathe by swathe with the scythe, and most of it was up in neat cocks, protected at the tops with crowns of a thick, green thatch of rushes. Some of the hay was still in little rounded mounds—'grasscocks' Peadar called them, or 'laps', because they were as much hay as a man or woman could hold between his or her half-crouching thighs and the circle of his arms and hands—waiting for one more warm, sunny day to be shaken out for a final drying and built into regular cocks, then stacks.

Finally one morning when a fine drizzle was falling Peadar heard his dog Fly whimpering impatiently beneath his bed. Dressing quickly and putting on an old tweed jacket he went out. A mist made it difficult to see the hill. Going back for his stick he went out again and quickly up to the crest of the hill and down the other side. There was no sign of the dog and the sheep were quiet. He worked his way back to the crest, then eastwards along it. He had been out almost an hour without any sign of the dog. Then for a moment the mist opened and he saw the dog several hundred yards to the east on his neighbour's land. The sheep were not in a bunch as he had seen them before, but scattered, and the dog had caught a lamb.

For a moment Peadar hesitated. If he set out now, at once, for the lowland farm, there was every chance that he would be there before the dog, and so prove that the dog was slipping his collar and away killing sheep. But how many more sheep would be killed if he left the dog alone? As the mist closed in again he made his decision, and headed for his neighbour's house. He called softly at a window of the thatch house much like his own. For a moment there was no reply, then came a low grunt Peadar knew to be a question.

'Come on!' he said. 'The dog's back. He's at your sheep. Handle him quiet. Don't put him away too quick. I would be there first, if I could.'

*

Standing in his doorway the large man looked at Peadar again, harshly.

'Back again,' he said.

'Your dog's up killing now. I left him and come straight here.'

The man looked at him for a moment, partly reflecting, partly clearing his still sleepy brain. The mist that covered the hills densely when Peadar set out had not yet begun to lift even here on the flat countryside. The air was chilly.

When he had pondered Peadar's statement for a moment the other man turned and went back into the house without closing the door, and Peadar stood before the blank open doorway. Then he returned. He had put on an old dark tweed suit jacket and carried a shotgun. Opening the gun he took a red paper cartridge from his pocket and, holding it for a moment above the breech, inserted it into the left-hand barrel, leaving the other empty. Glancing at Peadar, he closed the gun.

'If the dog's killing sheep, he'll be shot, and you'll be paid for the sheep. But if the dog is here, you're trespassing on this farm, not for the first time.'

Saying this he set his jaws together so that his jowls became prominent and the white grizzle of unshaven hair on his chin seemed to catch the diffuse silver light of the morning mist. His heavy neck was creased and red under the wrinkled cotton shirt, and his whole figure emitted the feeling of a man still not far from an interrupted sleep.

'You'll be trespassing on this farm,' he repeated, moving the gun very slightly, 'and looking to cause trouble.'

When he had said this he gave no sign of further movement, but stood quite still in his own doorway, the shotgun in his large right hand, its muzzle indicating the ground at Peadar's feet. Peadar looked at him. His mind tried to grasp the implied threat. 'Trespassing?' The word was never used in the hills. Sheep moved back and forth over an area of miles and farmers after them. No man objected to another passing over his land. Nor should the farmers here object. Peadar was puzzled.

The large man interrupted his thought. 'Will we go to the shed and see if the dog's there or away?' he asked.

'Your dog's away killing,' Peadar asserted. Then, as the other looked at him again without reply, he realized that the dog could be anywhere, that he had not actually tracked the dog this time in the heavy mist, but simply cut out in a direct line for the lowland farm, assuming the dog would stay behind. The other man watched him sharply.

'It's you who come here looking for trouble,' he said.

Peadar hesitated again. A light drizzle, something between mist and rain, had begun to fall softly from the northwest, and Peadar felt the soft, cool moisture settling on the side of his face and the outside of his hands.

'We'll go to the shed,' he said.

Telling about it later he remembered how the drops of falling mist had settled on the large man's hair and old tweed jacket in tiny glistening points of wetness that did not merge with each other or penetrate the surface they rested on but shone back the light each individually in a sparkling display. Peadar followed him to the shed, it too glistening with many distinct droplets of water along the roof and the green, moss-glazed stones of the north-facing wall. For a moment the two stood side by side at the door as the man cocked the loaded left-hand barrel of the gun, then removed the rusty sardine-tin key that held the iron latch in place and pushed open the door of the shed. In the grey diffuse light emitted by the wet mist through the small square window they could see, lying on the ground at the end of the short chain, beside the old cracked porcelain bowl, the dog's empty collar. For a moment neither man looked up. Peadar cleared his throat and coughed.

In the farmhouse kitchen, over tea and bread and butter, they quickly settled the price of the dead sheep. The large man took Peadar's word for the number killed, but they bargained briefly over their value. He had a shrewd idea of what each of Peadar's lambs would be worth that autumn, even without having seen them. Then he pulled a dense roll of wrinkled banknotes from his pocket and solemnly counted out the sum, note by note, adding some coins to bring the total to the amount agreed upon. Peadar fingered each note slowly, tentatively. He was still working over the sum in his head, laboriously adding the price of each sheep, one by one, to the previous ones. Then he matched the figure arrived at by this slow addition to the money in his hand. Holding one of the coins in his large blunt fingers, he seemed for a moment to be lost in some obscure and mysterious calculation. Suddenly he held out the coin.

'There's the luck,' he said.

The other man took the coin.

'What about the dog?' Peadar asked.

'You'll see him no more.'

Peadar nodded. Looking out the window he saw that the rain had stopped and the mist lifted. He looked at the money in his hand again. Folding it tightly he pushed it well down into the inside pocket of his tweed jacket. He looked about for his stick, which he had left in the corner near the kitchen door. Taking it up again, he left.

The rain had stopped. There was a peculiar warmth in the air for the lateness of the season. He was anxious to be home. Today would probably be the last chance to win the remaining hay. There would be good drying in it. His sister was probably already shaking out the grasscocks to dry. As he reached the foot of the hills he felt a gentle breeze across his face. A shotgun sounded in the distance. Above him two grey crows, flying irregular courses in the air, chattered loudly. As the haze thinned a weak, pale sun could just be seen in the east.

The Thatched Byre

The byre was in bad shape when I bought the farm. The roof was deeply crevassed where the old thatch had made way for the flow of rain in rivulets small or large, the back of it—the northern slope—covered with clumps of long grass, and the front pock-marked with cultures of mushrooms that spread more broadly day by day and grew again overnight when I pulled them out. Worst of all was that the wall at one end, the eastern gable, had fallen, leaving a gaping hole above which the rough roof beams, made from whole young trees, hung out like the ends of a huge rib-cage. At that end the scraws, the heavy grass and earth sods that make up the middle layer of a thatch roof, had fallen away, and the ragged shreds of thatch stirred continually with the breeze. It was a strange visual moral of the transience and decay of all human effort, as it stood outlined against the eternal high purple backdrop of Croagh Gorm—the Blue Stack.

Inside, the byre was just as it had been the day Petey and his family, the old owners, had moved to their new farm in the valley below. Cow dung hardened on to matted rushes, an odd sheaf of straw lying in a corner or wedged into the rafters, rotting half-used bags of moist and crumbling fertilizers, a remnant of cement that had become a stone. Under a heap of old straw and hay I found a potato that had sprouted and put out long, pale shoots, only the very ends of which ever saw the light, and at the base a cluster of perfectly formed but tiny tubers the size of marbles.

'I often had a mind to build that gable up again,' Petey said when he was showing me the farm. 'Two hundred of cement and the McHugh boys would have it up in the start of a day.'

He walked around the mound of heavy stones lying at our feet and pointed with one long finger.

'It was a bad old round stone in there that went and damn but the whole thing fell.'

Petey's neighbours took a different view.

'I don't know why Petey didn't keep a better coat of thatch on that byre,' Hannah Monaghan said. 'It's a good byre, you know. It's a shame to let it go down.' Then she added, 'You want good easings to keep the rain out of the walls. Once the water gets into them you're finished. They're sure to go down then.'

Petey's estimate of the cement needed—two hundredweight sacks—was more than sufficient. Rough stone walls are built up with a filling of gravel and clay to keep the stones immobile. Cement is hardly used. That is why the wall fell. Rain water seeping in at the top, where the thatch had got thin, gradually worked out enough of the clay to let the stones shift about. Then one day one of them, about two feet from the bottom, had shifted a bit too far and the whole thing fell.

But it took far more than what Petey called 'a start' to get the gable up again. The men insisted on tearing it down to its foundations for a good job, and they complained about the poor quality of the stones which made work slower than it would have been with good ones. It was true the stones were roundish and hard to build with. The weather was rainy too almost every day, and that slowed things down. One day the men arrived in the morning with a clear sky and then had to spend almost all the rest of the day sitting in our kitchen while the rain poured down outside. As the wall got higher they improvised a scaffold, fencing stabs on two old oil drums, and lifted each stone up first to the scaffold, then to its place on the wall.

I thought it a moving sight when, on a fine bright cold January day, Connie McHugh rolled the last large stone up the sloping wall of the rebuilt gable and settled it neatly into its crowning position. As he nudged it delicately into just the place he wanted it, I saw his thin hollow-cheeked kestrel face, tweed cap tilted across his brow, tan scarf knotted around his neck, outlined against a brilliant blue sky which was criss-crossed on that late winter afternoon with long cirrus clouds, vast wispy feathers of ice. As Connie, seeing them, foretold, the next day was rainy, threatening the unprotected newly repaired gable. But within another day I had replaced the missing wattles on the framework of beams, and put on the earth and grass scraws which were at least a measure of protection for the gable until the roof was thatched again. As soon as the weather dried up I got to work cutting the rushes for the thatch. The whole roof would need a heavy coat. One of the local farmers would have cut enough in two 'starts', but I was new to the scythe and it took me days. The rushes had grown freely in the years when the farm was not grazed, and they were long and heavy—hard to cut, but ideal for thatch. Jimmy Burke came by and showed me how to handle the scythe and how to gather the cut rushes in great sheaves and tie them with a cord of twisted rushes made on the spot and, when finally there were enough, he came by to thatch the old byre. He was known to be the best man at it in the region.

'Jimmy's very sore on rushes,' Hannah Monaghan said, meaning he used them heavily, 'but he does a wild good job.'

'It wants a middling good coat, you know,' Jimmy said as he started work, 'but it will do you five years then.' So the green thatch went on stripe by stripe, carefully combed out and smoothed by Jimmy's large fingers, until no seam or hollow could be detected, the whole an even, harmonious slope that would let no rain water lodge, but carry every drop away from peak and eaves and down beyond the walls. When he had finished thatching, Jimmy went half a mile away into the bog to cut and carry back creels full of a long sharp red grass he said would never rot, and matted it down over the ridge of the roof. Later, when the rushes had faded to the bright colour of straw, I could see from the hill above the farm the neat stripe of dark red grass running along the very top of the roof. The byre was safe.

After that Jimmy would often stop in on us for a chat in the evening as he was on his way 'to the cards' at Sweeney's. If there was a wind, he would ask if the byre thatch was well tied, since the ropes have a way of getting loose as the rushes settle, and have to be tightened from time to time. Otherwise the wind could get under the edges and tear the fabric of the thatch, or even lift the scraws. On very windy nights, Jimmy would tell the story of the great storm that almost carried the whole roof away late one night.

'The first I found was rushes hitting me in the face as I come up the lane. I put my light on the byre and I see all the thatch on the far end gone, and the wind lifting the scraws like a blanket. Man dear, it would take the whole thing, the whole roof.'

As he said this Jimmy raised and lowered his hands on an imaginary billowing swell of wind.

'Petey was away some road, over at McHugh's I think he was, and only Mary and the weans here. "Come on, Mary," I said, "the byre's going away".'

Jimmy puckered his lips, spat on the floor, paused for a moment, and then continued the story. By luck there was a length of new rope in the house, and he had tied a heavy stone to one end and thrown it over the billowing scraws at the west end of the byre. It had gone across and landed in just the right place to hold the scraws and thatch down, and then he and Mary tied the ends to wedges driven in between the stones of the walls.

Jimmy laughed with self-contentment. 'Didn't I tie that one well! It took a good while gettin' the knot out later on. And wait a minute, Petey had a heifer that time, and she was just calved, and she would take a founder, you know, with the wind comin' in, and a cold night. So I got a lock of sacks from Mary and tie them well round her. That kep' her warm, and she was that way until Petey got home, and to the next morning, and she was all right, the calf beside her. Deal a heat come on her.'

He pushed his open palms towards the floor, as if to say, 'I put everything in best order.'

Jimmy often told that story, and one night he even pulled it out when he and I were down spending the evening with Petey and Mary and their family on the dairy farm they had bought nearer in to town. Petey looked sheepish at hearing the recital of how he had been away from his farm at such a critical time, but we were all used to hearing Jimmy's tales of heroics and rescue. At times it seemed, to hear him, that there would not be a sheep living or a roof left whole all across those hills, if he had not been passing by at some crucial moment to save them.

Petey listened in silence, leaning his long thin frame casually forward, his hands lightly clasped, his forearms resting on his knees. He smiled when Jimmy finished the story they had all heard so often before, always identical, with hardly a word changed, and then he looked towards me.

We all leaned forwards to hear what Petey would say. That he was a 'slack man' there was no denying. How often he had told me so himself! How often I had come into his kitchen in the early afternoon of a fine, dry day to find him sitting before a cold grate, his grey hair uncombed and rough, a three-day stubble on his cheeks and jaw, his eyes dull with recent sleep. He was a man made to put off work, to turn his back on any pressing job until it was, first urgent, then imperative, and finally an emergency. Hence the byre.

But there was another side to Petey too. Not a model of activity most of the year, there were certain key moments in the annual cycle when he always managed to organize his long, thin frame for work. He knew just the right moments for potatoes, corn, hay and turf, and he was never without a full supply of them, the four essentials of life on a primitive farm. When it came time to set the potatoes, sow the corn, cut the turf, win the hay, Petey was always ready. The rest of the year was spent sleeping, sitting, drinking, and speeding the passage of time with a silver tongue.

If Petey's wife Mary had ever thought of trying to reform him, she had certainly abandoned the idea completely before I ever knew them. It is not likely that she did ever entertain such an idea. Like everyone raised on a rough hill farm, she accepted the character of the people around her as a fixed fact of nature, just as she accepted the nature of animals and all living, growing things as somehow fixed, unchangeable, not something to be modified at will, but something to be learned and accepted and worked with.

So she, and all the rest of the family, leaned forwards as I did to hear what Petey would say. They had heard it many times before, of course, his softly recited exorcism of the slur upon him, but I think the repetitions only made it the more enjoyable for them. The facts could not change, but Jimmy had put Petey in an awkward position, and Petey would have to outdo him. I knew he was too gentle to resort to nastiness, and I wondered how he would manage.

Petey looked over at me and began. 'I was at McHugh's that night. And the night was calm. By God, you would think no storm was to come that night.' And he added, 'No, you would not,' almost as if he were someone else corroborating his own statement.

He paused to look down and gather his thoughts.

'And I heard something hit the chimney, like a piece of metal, it sounded that loud. And I said, "There must be a wind." But you could hear no wind. It's sheltery down there. "Well," I said, "I must be going, to see all's right at home." "Wait a bit," Connie said, "I'll make some tea to help you over the hill." So we had tea, and then I got up to go. And I suppose we talked a while. I was on the floor just, ready to leave, you know, and in came Jimmy and told me about the byre. So off I went.'

Here Petey looked serious and gestured with his fore-finger to suggest promptness and dispatch.

'The wind was wild, right enough, but like Jimmy says, he saved the byre, and the heifer was all right too. I looked at her when I got back, and gave her a bucket and some hay, and she was all right 'til morning. The next day we put back the scraws that were off, and I cut a lock of rushes, and Jimmy thatched her, and we never had trouble more.'

Petey paused and smiled at me, and I could see Mary and the children all listening attentively, smiling attentively, waiting for the rest of the story they had heard so many times.

'The only thing in it, the wind wasn't bad until you got near the top of the hill coming from McHugh's. But it was wild at the shoulder. I had an old felt hat I used to wear that time, and as I got to the shoulder, didn't the wind take it away, and in the darkness I could not see where it went. I went out then to look for it the next day, and no sign of it. And I never could find it after that. Until six months later, I was in the bog, didn't I come on it stuck down in the ground. I was paring the bog to start cutting turf, and there it was stuck in the bog hole, in kind of soft wet ground.'

Petey paused again, recollecting, and smiled. 'And, by God, wasn't it all green with mould! I never could wear it more.'

Petey's whole account was as simple as that, and not much of it an answer to Jimmy's slur. But it was adequate to the purpose. As he finished, the whole family, waiting loyally for just that moment, laughed a long and satisfied laugh, filling the kitchen with the sound, until I, and Jimmy himself, joined in, and so resolved and settled and dismissed forever Petey's responsibility for the old thatched byre.

It was after midnight when we started getting ready to go, but we were delayed by the inevitable final cup of tea with bread and butter and marmalade. And before the tea the cows had to be milked—Petey's milking schedule had nothing to do with the early-to-rise early-to-bed pattern of farmers elsewhere. So it was about two in the morning when Jimmy and I set out on our uphill climb.

It was a dry night and enough moonlight filtered through the cloud cover for us to see our way without any light. For a long while we plodded along without talking, listening to the sound of our own steps in the noiseless night. As we reached the sudden steep uphill bend in the road that marked the beginning of the rise to Croagh Gorm, the Blue Stack, I felt the onset of the breeze that always blows in the treeless hills, and which divides them from the richer valley land below. Jimmy paused and looked around at the last few houses on that lower ground.

'Not a light,' he said. 'Not a light.'

I was puzzled by the remark and didn't answer. We walked on.

'They're all asleep,' he went on. 'Not a man up. And you see the way we haven't met a one on the road? Not a one.'

I wondered who Jimmy expected to meet on the road at 3 a.m., but I grunted a soft assent. We walked on along the ascending road, once more in silence.

'Not a one,' Jimmy repeated after a while. And then, as though he sensed my perplexity, he added, 'I remember the time there be ones up and down this road all night, until dawn, until morning they be comin' and goin'. Comin' and goin', you see, ramblin', to the cards and music and dancin' and all. Piles of them. Always.'

'All night?'

'All night. Piles of them.'

It was true. I had heard others tell me about the active foot traffic on the dirt roads all through the night, back in the days when the hills were populated, before the thatched houses had fallen into disrepair, and when there were families of twelve and fourteen and more in almost every house. A vigorous race that had worked by day and gone about looking for amusement by night.

I waited for Jimmy to continue, but nothing more was

said. We laboured on upward until we reached my door. 'I won't be comin' in,' Jimmy said, anticipating my invitation. Then he looked towards the byre. 'Want to keep a good coat of thatch on it,' he said. 'I'll be over one day soon to help you tie it again. Could be some of the ropes loose, you know. Never know when a wind would come and take all with it.'

Hired Man

The clocking hen puffed out her feathers and sounded a sharp, throaty *cluck*. With her mottled tan and white plumage raised from her body she seemed twice her real size. As she strutted a few steps forward in an attitude of special authority she clucked again and called her scampering brood of chicks in behind her. With a single movement of her claw she scratched the earth vigorously, then danced back two rapid steps, bending her beak and eyes quickly to the ground. Finding an earthworm, she raised her head and began a monotonous sequence of high insistent peeping noises, calling her chicks to the food. Only when they had all gathered in to her did she bend her beak again, seize the worm and begin tearing it apart with rapid shakings of her head. A plain white hen, hearing the shrill sounds, abandoned her scratching a few yards away and ran over to join the meal—unwary! Quickly the clocking hen puffed herself out even more broadly than before and, whirling suddenly, raced at the white hen, pecking at her head and crying out menacingly as she did so. As the white hen fled in alarm the clocker turned back to her brood and led them a few steps further off.

Nohar Peadar More watched the hen in fascination and amusement. Though he had seen the same events repeated spring after spring for years, since his childhood, he always wondered at the manner in which a normally inconspicuous hen suddenly took on a tremendous sense of self-importance and an abnormal courage as she felt the time coming to brood eggs and hatch chicks. For three weeks she would lie on the eggs, elaborately puffed out, careful to bring them all under the warmth of her body and her canopied feathers, seldom leaving the nest even for food, generating a feverish warmth. Then for six weeks more she would guard the chicks, lead them about, clucking them after her, teaching them to scratch, calling them to food, sheltering them at night and protecting them fiercely. The rooster himself, twice the weight and size of the hen, quickly learned to leave her and her chosen feeding grounds alone, and even the farm's dogs and cats stayed well away. For nine weeks in all the hen would achieve feats of vigour and courage and bluff she was quite unequal to the rest of the year. Then one day, very suddenly, she would lose the drive to clock, her plumage would collapse and she would return to her normal size. Back feeding with the other hens she would submit to their pecking and domination until she found her natural place again in the flock. Eventually even the chicks of her own brood, reaching full size nine months later, would face her one by one and test themselves against her.

As the clocking hen strutted away Nohar's eyes moved to another hen now at the opposite end of the cycle. Her usually brilliant red comb had faded in the course of only a few days to a dull, dark purple, the feathers of her tail had fallen out and oddly shaped patches on her body were bare and unprotected. She stayed away from the other hens and even when the crushed potatoes and barley meal was put out she made no attempt to join them in pecking up the food. She stood throughout the day with her body contracted and hunched, her head withdrawn almost into it, and her usually bright eyes mere slits of empty darkness, indifferent to the world and averse from it.

As he had wondered at the fierce, abnormal vigour of the clocking hen, so Nohar wondered now at the wintry withdrawal and torpid dullness of the moulting one. She scarcely seemed to breathe. Yet in a few days, he knew, her old feathers would be cast and she would be covered in a fresh bright set of new ones, and she would be as lively as she had been only a week earlier.

It was, he thought to himself, Nature—the nature of the beasts, the nature of all animal life—indeed, of all life, men and women included. He had often thought of the clocking hens and their magnificent bluff that enabled them to do so much more than their real strength entitled them to, to drive off larger animals with a purely temporary ferocity, to hatch and raise their brood through the apparent conviction of their own importance. And so had he, smaller, slower, less schooled than other men, and born into what was possibly the largest and poorest sheep-farming family anywhere in that part of the hills, made his way by determination through his life. There was of course the difference that Nohar used his head, not his instinct, and that he kept abreast of others with slow but careful work, not pretended ferocity.

Even from childhood he had fallen behind his other brothers and sisters. He remembered when his father had taken him to start at school. It was a clear, autumn day, one of the few good days in a cold and showery autumn, and Nohar wondered why he should be taken away on such a day instead of staying at home to help with the late hay. His father said nothing to him on the four-mile walk to the one-room school house, absorbed in his own thoughts, except to remark on the condition of the hay on some neighbour's farm, as they were passing, or on the quality of some unusual cow or sheep. The school was Nohar's first experience in a strange place alone, away from his home and large family or his own neighbours. Once he had been as far as the town, to a sheep mart, but that was with his father and older brothers and three score of their own wether lambs that they were taking out to sell, and he had been busy keeping the lambs together on the way to town and at the mart, and otherwise stayed close to his father and said nothing. Here in the school, when his father had left, he felt alone for the first time in his life.

Even the other scholars, boys and girls he knew from the chapel, seemed foreign to him. He had the sensation that they, without having to ask or be told, understood some secret thing about the school and its routine that he did not. When he had come in and handed the tall, neatly dressed man standing at the front of the room the two pieces of turf every scholar was expected to bring each day as his contribution to the fire, he had greeted him, as he had been prepared to do by his father, with one of the formulas of politeness usual in the hills, but it seemed that he had got a rebuff, a growled answer in return, in words he did not understand. In fact he understood nothing at all that morning, for the teacher talked in his own native English, a language Nohar had seldom heard and which he paid no attention to even when he did hear it. In the entire circle of his family and neighbours he had never heard anything but Irish, and his ear found the new and unfamiliar language so rough and odd as to be unlike human speech. As he listened that morning without comprehension to this strange, stiff, oddly dressed man, he thought the sounds coming from his mouth were much like animal ones. He understood nothing, and he took part in nothing. Others had been called on to stand up and reply, but he had not, and so he finally concluded that, not knowing the language, he had a certain immunity, a freedom from participation. Then the teacher spoke to him. In the silence of waiting that followed it was clear that he was expected to answer. The teacher motioned him to stand, and repeated his question. Nohar turned to the boy next to him to ask what he had said, but before he could hear the reply the teacher had spoken again.

'What does he say?' Nohar asked, in Irish.

But at that moment the tall man was upon him and he was being marched across the plank floor to the door and outside.

He had never forgotten the whipping that followed, for it was the only time he had ever been beaten, the only time in his life he had submitted to be beaten. The teacher had hit him only once, with a supple, slender rod that stung more than it hurt, and then explained in a strange but just understandable Irish that only English was ever to be spoken in the school. Nohar protested that he knew no English, and as he did so the rod came down again.

He felt an enormous surge of fury. The pain itself was slight, for he had experience with pain—burned at the fire, falling against rough stones, once even butted by a ewe when he had unwittingly come between her and her young lamb—but to submit to a beating by a man, another human being, and a stranger, was impossible for him. In an instant he found himself facing the astonished teacher, the rod in his own hand. He had no thought of striking back, even if the man did not tower over him, but he had already resolved in his mind that he would never again submit to a beating, and he had also resolved, as clearly and definitely as if he had spent a long while thinking the matter out, that he would never allow himself to be or go anywhere his own language was not allowed and spoken. In an instant he had thrown the rod down and run out of the school yard, turning up towards the hills, and home, and the waiting hay.

It was one of the few incidents in his life that he never laughed about. He did not go back to the school again. Fondness for his own language became ever stronger. Its strength, its humour, its music, the mysteries of its many legends, were close to him. Later, after he had learned to speak some English, enough to converse with the young people growing up on the farms around him, who did not know Irish well enough to speak it, or in order to carry on some business with people in the town, to whom Irish was completely strange, he sometimes, when the question of language came up, remarked proudly, 'I have very little English but the best of Irish.'

His reflections on the clocking hen and his recollection of his only day at school occupied no more than a second, but flashed through Nohar's mind so quickly he was almost unaware of them. He stood before his thatched house on the sloping side of a rough, heathery hill and his eyes ran slowly down along the valley below him observing the morning activities of a dozen or so farms, fresh thick smoke rising from low chimneys, cows being herded in for milking or being put out again to pasture, hens being fed, heavy creels of turf being carried in, by men bending under their load, to serve for fuel for the day, and he heard, faint and distant, the mixed sounds of those activities rising up the valley slope to where he stood. It was a misty, damp morning, and the finest of drizzles was falling slowly and evenly on to the glistening grass and heather, but there was a heavy stillness in the air and a warmth that suggested the onset of good weather. It was time, Nohar thought, to cut the turf for the year. He had made a start of it earlier but the weather had been too wet, and the cut turf lay in the downpouring rain while the oil washed out of it, leaving it a soaking mass that would be spongy and porous and quick-burning when it finally dried. Now he thought the good weather, the 'winning weather', the two annual weeks in May or June when even the showers common to the west of Ireland ceased entirely and a steady sun and wind dried the brick-like chunks of cut turf into a useable fuel, were near at hand.

As he mounted the hill towards the bog, Nohar's thoughts touched again on the reminiscences of his earlier life. Since he would not go to school and look for a better chance in life, there was no practical, no convincing reason for keeping him at home. There were too many already in the three room house, and not enough land for even a smaller family. At eight years he had been taken to his first hiring fair, lined up with the other farm boys and girls to be inspected, pawed, bargained over for six months of farm work, and—being small, it had taken most of the day—been taken into service and led away to a strange farm. Later he would boast of sticking it for six months with a farmer no one else had ever stayed with.

'Up early every day, to bed late. He had a pile of cattle and

33

a huge byre to dung every morning before I would get my tea. The time it took to take your tea, that was the time you sat, then out again in all weather, never mind what. Pra'ys* for dinner, tea for supper. When I got to my bed I found a cup of fresh milk. She put it there for me, you see, every night. At the end of six months, two pound ten. He would keep back ten bob because I had a pair of shoes from him and an old jacket, but I would have all, and he gave it me. I never went back more.'

So began his life as a hired man. One master followed another. Sometimes he worked for two farmers at once, sharing his work between them. As the time passed he grew gradually into the work. Thoughts of a better chance, anything connected with schools, study, books, men who spent their lives indoors and smelt more of hearth smoke than of open air and sheep, cattle, dogs and rain, did not much cross his mind. For reading and writing he saw no use, no practical application, and practical application was the governing rule of his observations of life. He tested himself against the work of the farm. He learned to like its constant variety as the seasons passed and the work begun in one part of the year came to fruition at a later one, providing store for even further on in time. No two years were alike, conditions changed, the change and variety were the only constants in a way of life that seemed unvarying, and what had been slow and hard one year became easy the next, or the opposite. As his growing up progressed, he faced the serious problem of making his way through life as a farmer without land, a hired man. His only assets were that he was willing to do any job he could do, and to learn new ones as he grew.

As he reached the bog Nohar planted his turf spade lightly into the soft turf at the base of the bank he meant to cut, reached into the pocket of his rough tweed jacket and pulled out a stumpy pipe, a block of dark tobacco and a small knife. Filling the pipe with chunks cut from the block and rubbed out on his heavy palm, he stopped to smoke before beginning

* Pra'ys: potatoes

34

the cutting of the turf, and he recalled as he lit the pipe the task he had been given of watching the old, bed-ridden woman every night. He was the youngest on the farm, and when the others went off to play cards, or to dance, or drink, he was expected to stay with her. He had heard that she had been a strong woman once, but now she was so slight he sometimes thought you might almost fail to see her in the bed. His first job every night was to fill her clay pipe and light it with a glowing coal from the hearth. As the smoke of the heaped, burning turf rose slowly, languidly up the open expanse of the high, broad, shallow fireplace, scarcely entering the opening above, but leaving a portion of itself behind to create a continual denseness of the air in the narrow kitchen of the old, thatched stone house, the boy had drawn heavily on the clay pipe to light it, far more heavily than was necessary, and the sweetness of the warm smoke of tobacco and turf mixed entering his mouth pleased him at once. Gradually, as he repeated the task night after night, alone in the house except for the frail old woman lying in her bed, the boy began to smoke more and more of the pipe before handing it on. Feeble as she was, the old lady was alert enough to know what was happening, and to find herself with a smaller portion every night. But in spite of her hurryings, in her little thin voice, or because of them, the boy managed to smoke the clay pipe faster and faster every night until—Nohar boasted laughingly years later—'I always had the best of it. By God, I had it well smoked before I give it her.'

Standing now at the strip of bog he meant to cut, already pared of grass and heather, Nohar paused, motionless for a moment, his turf spade in his hand. The valley mist had risen suddenly and was spread before him like a fine gauze. Through it the sun gleamed, a diffuse orange light, brilliant, almost blinding. Beyond it all the landscape of the valley was dimly visible still but without colour, a monochrome without contrast, a series of whites on white. A group of his own sheep near him became dim, nearly invisible forms, mere outlines, and the knolls and fields beyond them were more like a pale drawing than a reality. As the thin, rapidly rising mist dispersed, the colours returned in various delicate stages of faded dilution until once again they reached their normal appearance, accompanied by a bright, warm sun that boded well for Nohar's work that day of cutting turf.

'I have no one, on'y myself,' he thought, as he began tossing the dark brick-like lumps of cut bog from the end of the spade on to the bank. It was a phrase he often used when talking to younger people. He realized quickly that he must have been talking to himself, carrying on an imaginary conversation, to have that fragment of English run through his head. Work on a farm was meant to be done in company and became trebly hard and far slower alone. He remembered times in his days as a hired man when all the year's fuel for a farm had been cut and spread in a single day by three men working together at top speed. One had cut, one had loaded the cut turf on to the flat wooden turf barrow, with its single large wooden wheel, the third had wheeled it out in heaps to where it would be spread to dry. A single day had completed their work, but when the dry weather came all the women and children of the farm were out spreading the turf, turning it, standing the pieces on end supported against each other, and gathering the dry ones into little heaps, until finally the men returned to gather the won turf into long stacks—a second day's work for a whole year's fuel. No day of the year would pass in that climate of rain and damp without a fire on the kitchen hearth, indeed, one day's fire was lighted from the glowing coals, preserved in the warm ashes, of the day before. On the other hand, it was seldom cold enough even in winter to light a fire in one of the small hearths of the bedrooms. One fire, on the kitchen hearth, served for an entire family, no matter how large. The larger the better, in fact, since there was as much trouble in winning turf and heating a kitchen for one man as for a family of eighteen. More, perhaps, since a crowd of people in the kitchen made it all the warmer, apart from the many hands at the work itself.

Nohar could not have said what his thoughts were most of that morning as he repeated thousands of times and with an unvarying tempo and rhythm the motions of cutting the uniform chunks of turf and tossing them from the end of his spade lightly on to the bank above and beside him. An observer unused to the work he was at would have been impressed by the rapidity with which one piece of turf followed another, so that in a short while they were rising in a long high heap, as Nohar cut tier after tier of the bank. In spite of the repetition, the monotony of the unvarying process, or even because of it, he did not find the work tedious. His mind moved unceasingly along thoughts of his past life, his days as a hired man, and they too, his recollections, followed one another swiftly and effortlessly, seldom remaining with him for long, so that when he paused finally to smoke another pipeful he himself instantly forgot the content of his morning's thoughts, absorbed in contemplation of the work done and other practical concerns.

And then as he resumed the cutting of the turf after finishing his pipe, so at once, invited by the steady and rhythmical repetition of the work, his thoughts returned to their earlier channel. When the old lady had died there were other watching tasks for him: watching the hidden copper still, watching the cache of illegal whiskey from it, or delivering it in gallon jugs by night through the hills barefoot. He remembered a time when a man had been shot, then the arrival of soldiers, more shooting, alarm in the countryside, and quiet again. The rising and troubles touched him only that closely. As he grew he took on new jobs and always seemed to be suited to any farm work. He found he could mow hay or reap corn as well as anyone around. His lucky way with sheep and cattle became known and he was called in more and more to help at difficult calvings. When the time came to castrate the young ram lambs in August of every year, he did more and more of the work—in those days a short incision with a sharp knife and then pulling out 'the strings' with his teeth. Not every man could do the work properly. Some ruined the lambs, and as wethers they went lame or failed away. He had the knack of it, and he had powerful teeth and jaws.

By the common usage of the country the hired man was allowed to keep a certain number of sheep or cattle on the owner's land as part pay for his work. Nohar began to build up a flock of his own, even though hired out, and increased its numbers by renting more grazing land in the neighbourhood. His strength, his adept hand, his care with every job and his good humour were widely known, and he was always in demand to do work no one else could do quite as well. Because he liked the work and because he was lucky at it, and praised for what he did, he found satisfaction, almost contentment, even in being only a hired man. He was a man among men doing a man's work.

Nohar was lucky enough to have a strong memory. He could not write his own name, not even recognize it if he saw it written on an envelope addressed to him, but his memory was probably the more powerful for his lack of letters. When something interested him, when he had to follow specific instructions, he listened so intently that it seemed, to those watching him, that he was writing the words on his brain. It was natural for a young man whose only schooling had been farm work to think that for any given job there was only one right way of working, and that anything short of that right way was failure. That lesson was innate in the work. A cock of hay had to be so perfect in shape and texture that not a drop of rain would penetrate. A tiny amount of seeping damp could cast a mouldering musty taste on to the whole mass of sweet hay and make it unpalatable to cattle. A freshly thatched roof that allowed a single drop through would be a total failure, a source of derision of whoever had done the faulty work. Yet to do the job perfectly meant that every handful of thatch had to be applied in perfect order and regularity.

So it was with every job: castrating lambs, delivering a calf at a difficult calving, even tying an animal in its stall in the byre—a job done so many times in the course of the year— any carelessness was potential of disaster and loss.

With this insistence on perfection, on a single right pattern for every job, his mind grew precise and retentive. As he grew up judging animals and crops, so he came to judge men too. He sifted wise from unwise, and listened to and learned from those he respected. Years later his memory retained clearly the instances he had seen of right and wrong ways of working—the time he had seen the sheep dipped in cold, stormy weather, and their failing condition after that; or another time when he had been one of three young men obliged to hold a flock of sheep together on the hills for three rainy, windy days and nights waiting for a calm day to dip them. 'Thon man knew what was right,' he would comment even years later when talking about dipping sheep and its ins and outs. The right procedure was obvious there and necessary in everything. Once he had learned such a lesson, there was no repetition of experiment for him. The first instance stuck in his head as the practical standard from which he would not deviate. Gradually he amassed a large number of such instances, a mental reference book to be read only within his own memory, full of lore, the lessons of his own observation, the teachings of the past.

From the old people he had learned that when the high hill lakes were black and restless the year would be one of storms and failing crops, scarce hay and sickly animals. They taught him to observe the badgers in the spring, and whether they were 'settled' or 'restless'—hooking out the grass on the meadows and burrowing in places they had avoided before— which meant weeks of heavy rain ahead. From them he learned to observe the cunning of the fox, who never frightened the young lambs but rolled playfully on his back and frolicked with them until he was ready to carry them away to his den with its waiting, hungry brood. It was part of that unwritten body of essential knowledge to know that a hen that crowed like a rooster was a sign of disaster and had to be killed, and that black spots on the young lambs' fleece was a forerunner of some bad luck.

Luck and practicality were the two great considerations for failure or success in work and life. Bad luck could come any time, or the reverse, and some times a man made his own luck, good or bad. And there were deeper secrets, the power of some priests to raise the dead, to make murdered men say who had killed them, and to still their lips. It was all part of the great plan and cycle of Nature, great Nature that gave rise to all living things and took them back again in time to become the material substance of her next progeny. All these things were talked of by the hearth around the smoky fires on the wet winter nights by 'the old people', and Nohar listened and remembered.

After a while, when he had mastered all the work of the farm, listened to the talk of the old people for many years, seen their practices and recorded in his memory what had succeeded and what had failed—after, in short, he had collected a vast practical experience of farming, his satisfaction with the life he had happened into began to wane. The work pleased him, he could always find a good place and get a good wage, he was well treated, liked, in demand—but, he was a hired man. It was a road that led nowhere. He could not think of marrying and of a family until he had a farm and a house of his own, and cattle, and a flock of sheep.

Looking up briefly from cutting the turf, Nohar caught sight of the figure of a man plodding slowly across the brow of the opposite hill. He paused to examine the distant form, looking for signs of identity. Heavily slow-moving the distant figure made its way across the far slope and down to the stream that bounded Nohar's land, then slowly upwards through the broad, steeply rising meadow lands, past the sheds and byres and upwards still towards the house, not stopping there but continuing past it and on towards where

Nohar was working. The two men greeted each other. Nohar glanced at the ragged looks of his guest, the torn jacket and missing buttons—so that the jacket was tied round with a rough bit of cord—the uneven patches on the pants, and the split boots. He put aside his turf spade and the two men returned side by side to the house. As Nohar revived the dying fire on the hearth from its few live coals, and got ready some tea and bread, they chatted about the topics usual with farmers—the season and the chances for a spell of dry weather, the prices asked and given for animals at recent fairs and marts, the growth of grass on the meadows and of the grain, and so on to the illnesses, deaths and births, emigrations and returns, and the general fortunes of their neighbours, the two men's voices contrasting softly and strongly as they spoke, Nohar's mild, almost purring tone rising at moments of emphasis to a near shout in the smallness of the thatched house, the other's voice a high, hoarse, plaintive call, with a warbling in it like the cry of a curlew. He was a man known for his hard labour and very poor luck. Most of the winter he toiled on the county road-crew, gravelling the untarred roads, returning late and by dark, on foot, sometimes a distance of miles, in rain or snow or whatever weather came, ragged and badly clothed at any time, to a supper of potatoes, bread and tea and milk. His diet was seldom varied, a repetition day after day of bread, tea, potatoes, butter, milk and sugar, and on that he sustained his strength and laboured to support his wife and four children. Alone on his large hill farm, working on the roads throughout the winter, keeping a large flock and several cows, trying to manage all himself, he was always behind, and his lands and buildings had an appearance of neglect, the suggestion of never enough care.

His visit to Nohar had a double purpose: to welcome the hired man home again, and to ask a favour—a day of cutting turf.

'You've made a great change here,' he remarked briefly as Nohar poured the tea from the soot-encrusted tin pot that had been standing on a little mound of hot coals heaped on the hob. 'You're a powerful worker,' he added, starting to sip hastily, in small sips, at the hot tea.

'You're welcome to a day anytime I can give you one,' Nohar answered.

A day of cutting turf. It was not heavy work for him, and he knew he could ask a favour in return, help with sheep perhaps, dipping or dosing them, when an extra man would be welcome. He would be glad to work away from home and interrupt the solitude of his own work, and he knew that his cutting of turf would be welcome to more than one family, for the shortage of turf on the neglected farm was often made up for by late-night visits to neighbours' stacks. It was, they always said, not the loss of their own fuel that bothered them so much as the ragged condition of the thatch after the clandestine visits, a raggedness that left the remaining stacked turf at the mercy of any shower that came and rendered it, if the damage was not discovered and repaired, a soggy damp mass that would smoke but not burn when put on to the fire. The raggedness of the thatch was a hallmark, however unintentional, of the secret visitor.

The two separated and Nohar, promising the other man the next good day that came, returned to his bank of turf. The day he would give his neighbour now was a day without pay. It was a situation that pleased him, to be working as one neighbour for another, and not as a hired man for a wage. For long he had not been able to see how he would achieve his own farm. One of eighteen brothers and sisters, almost the youngest of them, he could not find a place on the family farm. Land was hard to get, and though the living from it was a poor one the price of buying it was high. The transition from landless man to independent farmer was not through being a hired man. It was far better to go away to the cities and work at building or in the tunnels or on the roads and save enough to buy a farm when you returned. But in fact few of those who left came back, and never to farming. At any rate, Nohar knew, there was only one kind of work he was suited for. He could not go away.

But suddenly there had come a chance. When his father died the family farm was found to be heavily in debt—no one was certain how much, something between a hundred and three hundred pounds—at a time when a cow sold for three pounds, a wether lamb for two shillings and six pence. The farm itself was badly run down after years of neglect. Tall thick rushes covered the meadow, making a crop of hay impossible. The fences had decayed and the sheep and cattle of the neighbouring farms wandered across the land picking it bare of grass. The thatched rooves of the house and the byres were black and crevassed, some of them almost beyond repair. The flocks that had once covered the square mile of rough grazing on the hill were scattered and depleted to a remnant that was not enough for even a smaller farm. Nohar had thought that some of his older brothers would take over the farm, but now, unexpectedly, there were no takers. Some were in England, some America, two had farms of their own, and of the three who were hired out like him none wanted to face the indefinite sum of debts. It was a doubly unexpected chance for Nohar, since normally the farm would not be his until all his brothers and sisters and any other relatives who might have a right to inherit some part of the property had signed away his or her share and so made way for the new owner, a process that could take years, or perhaps never be achieved, with so many to sign, and those so widely dispersed around the world. He knew little about law and solicitors but he had heard of farms disputed among relatives for so long that in the end the solicitors had declared in court that the matter need not continue, since legal fees had consumed the value of the land. But now, with the farm encumbered and the full sum of the debt unknown, no one would claim a part of the property, and Nohar could acquire the farm merely by accepting the debt with it. He had only to sign, a formality carried out for him by one of his sisters in the presence of a

43

solicitor and a witness. He had paid the known debt of £130 and accepted responsibility for any other claim that might be made and justified, but the farm was his.

He returned to a mass of problems. From inside the sagging roof of the old house, soot and cobwebs hung in heavy dark curtains two or three feet deep, matted in places by the rain that penetrated the rotting thatch. There were no fences to hold his own flock or cattle, or exclude those of his neighbours. The interiors of the sheds and byres were wet and almost unuseable, and the meadow was overgrown with rushes so tall and thick that, as Nohar often bragged later, 'they were coming from every direction and hauling and carting them away for thatch, even over the hills. There were none that high for miles.'

He had cleaned out the inside of the old house with handfuls of sand hurled at the beams, until he had brought down every bit of soot. The rushes from the meadow, toilsomely cut by hand with a heavy scythe and gathered into sheaves tied with a cord made from the rushes themselves, went on to the rooves of the buildings in thick coats of green thatch that he knew would last for years. Flagstones carried from the burns and streams had repaired the cracking, uneven floors. Rotting lintels and windows were replaced by a local carpenter. A start was made on the fences, to keep animals out of the fine grass and save it for a crop of hay. The heavy work had not been as heavy as he had thought it would be. Each day's progress invigorated him and prepared him for more work. He seldom felt the need of a day off.

His big problem was stock. He had inherited a square mile of land, more than six hundred acres of rough grazing, and his own hired man's flock could hardly fill it, but without fences he would have trouble keeping bought-in ewes. And there was the problem of the price. Finally he knew he could only solve that problem the hard way, by buying ageing ewes at a low price and 'haunting' them to his land—keeping them shepherded within his own boundaries until they settled down. Their age was not such a serious problem. A 'change of grass' had a tonic, rejuvenating effect on sheep. The problem of keeping them together was more serious. Searching for a single lost sheep could be as time-consuming and laborious as herding a whole flock.

It was the only possible solution, and he accepted it, threw himself into the job vigorously, as part of the adventure of his personal independence in the domain of his own republic, his farm. When he had bought the ewes, finding them in odd groups here and there on different farms around the country-side, he had a busy time of it keeping them together for the first eight or ten days. After that his knowledge of their habits and the direction each ewe would take to wander off in made it easier for him. He knew the ewes would stay put in calm, settled weather, but that wind and storm set them moving, first in search of shelter, then back towards their old haunts, the ground they knew. On such stormy days he was up and on the hills early, and stayed out long, crouching at times as he mounted the brows and crests before the force of gale winds, turning his back to squalls of hammering hailstones, sheltering beside high banks of turf from the driving rain, but always keeping the flock together.

More debts had appeared, all of them small ones, until a shopkeeper in the town had asked for £182. Nothing at all had been said of the debt for months after his return. It was a question whether anything would have been said, except for the fact that in the spring Henderson, the owner of the shop, had decided to sell out and was collecting everything owed to him. It was arranged casually. One day when Nohar was in the shop, Henderson had opened the large credit ledger that always lay on the counter, and showed him the total. The figures did not mean anything to Nohar, but neither did he think to question them. The debt did not surprise him, only the size of it, which showed how long it had been building up. It had been years since anything had been paid for. A week later he was back in the shop carefully peeling wrinkled one-pound notes from their tight roll, the long-saved contents of an old screw-cap jar. As the count slowly mounted, first by ones, then by scores, until he reached nine score and two, the bills piled up in a scattered heap on the counter. Other farmers, standing awkwardly about in the narrow space between the counter and the racks and shelves of goods, half empty against the opposite wall, seemed neither to notice the transaction nor to be ignoring it. A slight crouch, a slight bending at the knees and flexing of forearms and thick fingers, suggested rather men who were ready to take hold of a heavy burden than shoppers waiting their turn. Two women from the town exchanged a rapid and knowing glance, silently confirming to each other their often repeated assertion that the hill farmers were all rich. When Nohar had finished, Henderson gathered in the bills and put them away without another count.

Nohar felt certain then that he had met the last debt, but having paid it he was left with little cash. His long savings were gone. No matter! His ewes were heavy in lamb by then, in a few months he would have young lambs to sell. A cow had calved at Christmas. A farmer in the valley below him had sent up forty sheep for summer grazing at two shillings a piece. His farm would soon be earning.

Thinking about the payment of the final debt and calculating the margin of remaining cash before the earnings of the year would start, Nohar realized that he was near the end of the final, lowest floor of the bank of turf. It was the richest, darkest turf of the bank. Full of oil, it would be the easiest won and the hottest on the hearth, burning away into a deep red ash that, mixed with grease, would make the mark he rubbed into the fleece of his sheep at the back of the shoulders. And although the turf was the best, it was also the easiest cut, for it was well below the level of the matted roots that clogged the spade at the higher floors.

Stopping for a moment, Nohar looked down over the land before him, the growing meadow grass, the bright green tops of his broad crop of potatoes, the lighter green of the sprouting corn, where he had dug the fresh ground out of grass and sown four stone of seed oats, and his mind made quick but rough calculations: two-score cocks of hay, three-score measures of potatoes, half a dozen ricks of corn. He would need little that winter, for the farm itself would supply almost all in the way of food and fodder. As his neighbours often put it, he 'had all within himself.'

Nohar kept his promise the following day, cutting turf throughout the long clear morning and afternoon. The ragged man's three young sons, all still boys, loaded the cut turf on to the low wooden barrow and took turns manfully wheeling it away from the bank and dumping it in heaps where their sister was spreading it out on the drying ground. Offered a day in return, Nohar merely asked for two of the boys to be sent, the very next day, to help him spread his own turf.

The drying weather had come. All through the following morning he wheeled his cut turf, while the two boys helped to load the barrow and spread the dumped mounds.

'Keep spreading you now,' Nohar said at last, when he saw the job almost done, 'and I'll make the tea. When you see me hoist the red flag before the door, come down as fast you can for your tea.'

'Now,' he said as they ate, 'it's a good job to have that done. It's time anymore. I'll be off to the hill now. I must get Bryce's grazers together. He'll be up tomorrow looking to have them clipped.'

The boys stayed with Nohar as he climbed the high slope behind the house and went all around the rough hill ground beyond it gathering in sheep, carefully separating the ones he wanted from those he meant to leave, bringing them down as a small flock, ewes and their lambs together, to where he would herd them in between the old walls of a roofless, crumbled house.

'It's late now. I'll leave them here for the morning,' he said finally. 'Bryce himself will be up.'

But he did not mean to wait for Bryce. Early the next day he started the shearing, opening the long, heavy fleece down the front of the ewes, deftly clipping where the new and the old wool met, rolling the fleece systematically back and away from the body of the sheep in an even, dense mat, as though he were removing a heavy winter overcoat by degrees. Folding each fleece and tying it with two strands of itself, he stacked them on a shelf of dry ground beside the old walls, pausing to look down the valley from which the morning sounds were rising. Finally, when the accumulated fleeces had formed in three soft columns along the wall and most of the ewes stood oddly bare and naked-looking inside the stone enclosure, he saw Bryce coming up the road, a smaller figure at his side.

'That will be his girl Hannah,' Nohar said softly to himself. 'She's growing up now.'

'Your sheep mostly done, Charlie,' he called from where he was cutting free from a ewe the last bit of her wool. 'You have no call for them wool-shears, I'll soon have them done for you.'

Bryce and his girl stood looking over the low wall at their sheep.

'They done well on the hill, Nohar,' Bryce commented at last.

'Oh aye, Charlie. They're thick fat. They done well.'

As Bryce and Hannah watched he sheared the final ewe, proud to show off his skill and care, his excellent long-studied ability to handle animals and have them thrive, his powerful but gentle strength that controlled the animals masterfully but quietly and never hurt them. He was conscious of Bryce's daughter, born in the years he was away, half a woman now but still half a girl, looking on.

'How are the weans, Charlie?' he asked.

'Nine of them now, Nohar. Takes plenty to feed them.'

There was a silence while neither man spoke and only the soft, rhythmical sound of the wool-shears working along the open seam of the fleece was heard, and the occasional restless shifting of the sheep within the pen. Nohar glanced from time to time at Hannah's round face watching him intently as he worked. She would soon be old enough to marry, he thought. Nine weans. 'Plenty to feed,' Bryce had said. But good to have, too, a wife and children, now that he was owner of his own farm.

'You'll find a wife yourself one of these days,' Bryce said.

Their thoughts had crossed. 'Oh, aye,' Nohar answered casually. He was finishing the last ewe. He folded and tied the final fleece and released the ewe.

'Put out ewe with lamb,' he said. 'Here'—catching a ewe—'take you this one, I'll get the lamb.'

Putting the ewe and the lamb together outside the pen, they let them away. The puzzled lamb examined the naked gleaming body of its mother, whose swelling udders, no longer covered by a long curtain of dense wool, within whose darkness the lamb had learned to search for milk, now stood open to the air. Slowly the lamb realized the change, accepted the bare sheep as his mother, tentatively sucked at the exposed teat and then fell in behind her as she slowly, grazing as she went, made her way upwards. Two by two they put out the remaining sheep.

'There. That's all now,' Bryce said as the two men and the girl stood watching the small flock gathered densely around the narrow gate that kept them from the rough hill-grazing. Nohar opened the gate, and the sheep filed through and started upwards.

'You're a good hand at it, Nohar,' Bryce said again as the three stood looking upward at the sheep slowly spreading out. 'It's good to have you back. I doubt it wasn't all fun, away.

49

You would get tired of it too, I suppose, hired out.'

The sun was high. As the three moved towards the low thatched house, they paused again to look at the sheep rising and dispersing in intermittent rhythms of grazing and walking, steadily higher on the steep, irregular ground of the high hill.

The Yellow Dog

The dog came towards me with a motion that was a squirm and a crawl together. His belly dragged the ground, and his tail and all his hind parts wagged hopefully for the friendship his eyes, looking up at me with a kind of fear in them, seemed to be pleading for.

'Is this the dog?' I asked.

His fur was that light rust or orange colour we talk of as red hair, and so often associate with Ireland. At home, in America, I would have called him a brown dog. Here in the Donegal hills, I found out later, he was a yellow dog. As I watched him squirming towards me, his belly so low to the ground it seemed as if he was almost afraid to stand at his real height, with that look in his eyes of hope filled with fear, I thought to myself, 'At least he'll be friendly.'

'Will he make a good sheep dog?' I asked.

'The best,' Mickey Paddy answered. I had never seen Mickey before. My neighbours knew I was looking for a dog, and one of them had come to me that morning to tell me Mickey had a pup for sale. Following directions I made my way down to where he would be working at turf every good day and found him quickly from the description they had given me, and from the two dogs that were with him.

'That's the mother over there. You see the way she sits looking at the sheep? She always has her eye on them. He'll be the same. It's in his blood.'

I looked more closely at the dog. I knew that the local

51

farmers might tell me the truth, or not. Certainly they knew they could tell me anything. But that made little difference. Having no skill or knowledge to go on, I was determined to go on luck. I knew it could work out just as well in the end. Looking a second time at the dog still hovering about my feet, squirming hopefully, I noticed that the hair beyond his ribs and around his haunches was missing, and instead there were large patches of grey, scaly scabs. The sight reminded me how often I had been told that it was hard to find a good dog.

'What's the matter with him there and there?' I asked.

'I don't know,' Mickey answered. 'He took an itch, and I got some powder in the town that kind of burned him.'

I didn't know dogs, not even enough to know that the dog had been starved. His hair was falling out of him from hunger. I found that out only after I had taken the dog. I went down to Paddy Wee Jack's thatch house then—he was one of Mickey's near neighbours, and it was he who told me, on my way to Mickey's the first time, that the dog had the makings of a good one—and asked him again. I was new in the hills and didn't know who to trust. I watched Paddy closely to see if he had been lying to me.

'Why did he lose the fur?' I asked.

Paddy's face, his cheeks full of tobacco juice that appeared in small, dark bubbles at the corners of his lips, fell into that position of mournful sadness it always wore when any even slightly sad subject came up.

'S'pose he never had anything on'y the mother's milk,' he said.

'What? For six months?'

'S'pose not.'

So that was it. I knew that one neighbour would not criticise another to an outsider like me, but Paddy had gone far enough to let me know that the dog had been starved.

But that was after I had taken the dog. Looking at him at my feet desperately pleading with his wagging rear end for a master, I decided I had better take him. I felt no sympathy for the dog, nothing but a slight repugnance at the thought of the lice and worms and fleas he might be bringing with him to the farm, but in my mind was the thought, 'At least he'll be friendly,' and I knew that was a good sign in a sheep dog.

'How much do you want?' I asked.

'Thirty bob will do.'

'All right. Does he have a name?'

'Toby it is I have on him.'

'Good. I'll call for him on Friday. Is that all right? I want to fix up a place for him.'

Mickey's face fell slightly.

'Friday? All right. Friday then.'

I had it in mind to make a house for the dog, of wood—'craw' they call it in the Blue Stack—but there was so much to do early in May, with a first summer of farming ahead of me, that I never got around to it in the few days I had. I decided to put the dog in the byre, where he would be warm, even though I didn't like to think of the worms or worse he might carry in with him. Friday afternoon I went down to get the dog. My idea was to take him to the vet to get him wormed, and I had someone meet me with a car. I remembered to take along a couple of thick pieces of bread, thinking that his friendly look would be even more friendly when he saw them. I had no wish to pet, or even touch him, until I was sure the worms were out of him and the mange at least being treated. The bread, I was sure, would win him at once.

This time it was raining, and I had to go all the way to Mickey Paddy's house. I looked expectantly for the friendly, hopeful dog, but didn't see him. Mickey came out of the small, thatch house.

'Here's your dog,' he said, going to a tin shed built on to the gable of the house.

Then I saw the dog, but his posture and attitude were different from what they had been the first time I saw him. Now he was tied to a large rock by a strand of wire that gleamed greyly in the dim light of the shed. I saw that he was tied tightly, his neck close to the stone and his feet and claws spread out as if he were trying to clutch the ground, to keep himself from being dragged into it, or away from it, I didn't know which. Now there was nothing friendly about the yellow dog, only a kind of terror and hostility, irrational and blind. I thought suddenly of an injured dog lying in the wet New York gutter one autumn night, its hind legs smashed by a car. 'Don't go near him,' my father had called—but a moment too late: the dog had already bitten my hand. Now this dog, tied so closely there, seemed suddenly no longer to have that one advantage I had looked for in him, that he would be friendly. His face snarling with fear reminded me of that injured animal of years before. Hastily I threw the two pieces of bread at him, afraid to approach. The dog gobbled them quickly, so quickly he almost didn't seem to chew them. It happened suddenly, he had no idea where the bread had come from. I understood then that a whole loaf would have made little difference.

Mickey twisted open the wire that was around the dog's neck, lifted him by his two front feet, and carried him dangling and stiff with fear to where I stood.

'Will he bite?' I asked.

'I don't think so,' Mickey said. 'You don't have to worry.'

He put the dog in the back of the car that had come to meet me, and I got in to hold him. At Letterbarrow I tied the bit of grass rope Mickey gave me to the dog's neck, and the other end to the wire fence outside the post office, and went in to call the vet. When I came out a few minutes later, the dog was gone. A bit of grass rope was dangling from the fence where I had tied him. Later on I learned how quickly he could cut even a thick rope with his teeth. He was gone for two days and no one saw anything of him. Then, early on the third morning, Amby Meehan, the Letterbarrow taxi man, saw a strange emaciated yellow dog prowling around near his house. After his two extra days of hunger, the dog was more skeletal than ever, and the grey scaly patches of bare skin

were still more conspicuous against his ?
fur. Amby's first impulse was to get ?
the dog. Then he changed his mind,
pan with bread and milk, and pu?
afterthought, he tied up his own dog. Lat?
out from Paddy Wee Jack who owned the dog,
him up to me. I often wondered later why he ha?.
his first impulse and shot the dog. He must have kno?
the dog had no owner, or he wouldn't have been left in ?
condition. No doubt it was something he saw in the dog's
breed, in the shape of his head and face, that made him think
he had the makings of a good sheep dog, too good to shoot.

'Worm that dog, and get him some vitamins,' he said in a
voice hoarse from an unbroken chain of cigarettes, 'and you'll
soon have a good dog. You can see it by his head. He'll be
a good one. Look at him.'

I did look at Toby, many times a day, but his good qualities
eluded me. Skeletal, mangy, frightened and dull, he showed
no interest at all in sheep. The first time I took him around
the inland pasture with me—on a lead, because he wouldn't
come otherwise—the ewes moved away from him in alarm,
but by the next day they were all fully aware of his harmless
nature, and ignored him. I soon discovered, in fact, that he
was thoroughly afraid of them.

But that was natural enough for a dog in that starving and
feeble condition. As soon as I got him home, I tied him up in
a corner of the byre with some straw to bed down on, and
brought him a dish of bread and milk. It was a middling
portion—I did not want to feed him too much all at once.
Toby swallowed the food in great gulps that were like inhala-
tions. He didn't stop to chew or taste, his aim was to get the
mush into his stomach as instantly as he could. Then he
quickly licked the yellow plastic dish. Then he belched once
or twice and vomited up most of the meal. He ate that again
almost as quickly as he had the first time, and then vomited
it again. As he was eating it a third time, I left him alone.

ame back a few hours later, he was snoozing on the
aw I had left there for him, just as I had left it, not
ged or pawed about at all. After a few meals he stopped
ing, but his appetite remained ferocious. One morning
und he had chewed up and eaten a large chunk of his
dow plastic dish.

The next day I took him out with me, a long line of grass
rope tied to his neck and trailing behind him. The precaution
was not needed. Toby walked slowly, without enthusiasm or
spring. It was May, and I was cutting turf for the first time
in my life. It was an agonizing effort. I couldn't understand
how it was possible for one man to cut enough turf to last a
whole year. While I worked, Toby would lie on the bank near
me, his eyes directed blindly away, his head slightly raised
towards the sun, or else he would lie on his side and sleep. He
seemed to be deliberately trying to drink in the hazy sun, as
I remembered myself further south often lying in the sun on
the first warm days of May, trying to absorb sun and warmth
after the winter. So he lay there, day after day, dozing in the
weak sun that filtered through the high clouds. From time
to time I would look over at him, hoping to see him shift and
stir, make a few half turns and coil freshly into a new position,
but he never did. He lay, still and extended on his side,
soaking up such sun as he could get. I wondered if he would
ever sit up and watch the sheep the way the mother dog did.
He paid no attention to them when they wandered by, and
they ignored his presence. I noticed that his pale, yellow eyes
did not seem to be focused on anything at all.

For several weeks Toby showed no inclination to run, much
less jump. It was only after two weeks that I saw him take his
first leap, and that a short one. But gradually he began to
grow more alert, as the vitamin pills and liberal feeding took
effect. His coat began to thicken and grow smoother, his eyes
brightened and his step became brisker and more flexible. He
began to lie not on his side, as before, but on his belly, his
paws out straight before him, his head raised to the sun. I had

56

had him for a month when I first felt sure that there was a real improvement in his condition. The fur had not returned to the bare spots, but he was less bony and walked with a livelier, padding step. And it was then, when he was just getting on his feet, that the qualities of the dog as I was later to know them, the first signs of his character, which till then had been smothered by debility, began to appear.

Toby took to wandering off without notice, and though I had taught him to come in when called or whistled to, he would often disappear while I was working at turf, and refuse to return. At such times, I often found him lurking hidden behind a bank of turf not more than a few feet away, listening to me whistle and call, as loud as I could, hunting for him in every direction. From time to time I noticed Toby staring at me, while I worked, with a peculiar intensity, a kind of interest, it seemed to me, and puzzlement too, as if he understood what an enormous effort I was making to get out the year's turf, and wondered what I was at. There was a kind of pitying look in his eyes, I sometimes thought, or a mocking one. What fools these mortals are, he seemed to be thinking. And then when he saw me observing him in return, he would turn his head away, settle his chin on his paws, and resume his snooze in the sun.

It was that way of lying and watching, seeming to reflect, or even meditate, while he was observing me all the while, that first made me improve my opinion of the dog. 'There must be something to this dog,' I thought. I know now that he really was observing me, and from time to time he evidently came to conclusions. That came out sharply one day in July. Jimmy Burke had come to cut turf for us. With his usual energy, he had started at ten in the morning, and at six in the evening he still showed no signs of flagging. He was on his third bank of turf, and it was becoming clear that he meant to cut half a winter's supply of fuel for us before he stopped. It was up to me to spread the turf as he cut it—every one of the thousands of pieces—that was what Jimmy expected, and it would have been too much to let him down, in the face of all his own work that day. Pride kept me at the work, though my back and arms were painful and stiff.

Suddenly, standing on the brow of the bank of turf, I looked about and realized that Toby had gone. I had kept him in sight all day, but now he had slipped away. I began to whistle, then call. Jimmy stopped his work and looked on curiously. His face showed his amused expectation of learning something—about the dog, no doubt, and about me as well. Our eyes reached out across the landscape in every direction. Bits of rough heather, spots that some kind of blight had touched and turned brown, caught our eyes, and tufts of rough, red grass. I looked for any movement of red or brown in among the areas of green, or for signs of uneasiness among the sheep grazing the meadows below us, but saw nothing. All was still. I whistled again.

'Funny he don't come in when he hears you whistling him,' Jimmy remarked, 'and you feeding him like that.'

He put the turf spade in position to begin work again.

'He'll soon come back,' he said. 'He's not far off.'

I decided to give one last whistle, as loud as I could. Then, as the pieces of turf began flying on to the bank again, I saw Toby at last. He was lying perfectly still behind a clump of tall, heavy rushes, not twenty feet away, peering through them with an expression of intense, bemused curiosity. I saw in his eyes at once that he had made a great discovery. He was still just taking in the fact that I could fail to see him, even when he was face to face with me. He had discovered his own protective camouflage. But he had discovered something more important—that he was shrewder than me, and that there were ways he could fool me when he wanted to.

Toby's colour deepened as his fur grew back. He took to cleaning himself, carefully licking off his wet paws when we came in from the bog, and gradually extending his attention to all the rest of his body that he could reach, twisting his head and stabbing out his long tongue to brush and clean his breast, that grew brighter and fuller with every week of good feeding. He fought a long battle against the insect pests he had picked up in his early days. Even dipping him in sheep dip and dusting him liberally with lice powder never stopped them for more than a few days or a week. But finally he succeeded by himself, by his own persistent and meticulous care of himself, in banishing them.

With good feeding (and the eggs he learned to steal from the hens' nests) his fur grew longer, thicker and redder. But the bog itself, instead of turning green, as it should have in May, became redder. The nights were frosty, the grass and fresh heather were not growing, and Toby remained camouflaged when he was on the hill. His way of disappearing—it was not often, once a week perhaps—bothered me, but I was even more worried by his indifference to sheep, and I began to grow impatient. Of course, there was no reason to expect him to work before he was a year old, or even two, but there was always in my mind the thought that I could be raising this mangy dog, that no one else would have, to no purpose at all. Was I going to be made a fool of?

One day I was chasing some ewes that had grown used to grazing my fields in those years when there was no one to mend the fences, and one of the ewes got her horns caught on the wire on her way through the rotted-out spot in the fence she always came and went by. I managed to get hold of her, and tossed her over into a sitting position. Then I whistled for the dog. Toby approached tentatively, hesitant, puzzled. I called him again softly. He came a few steps nearer and stopped, his head and nose extended forward, sniffing from a distance of several feet. Gradually he realized he could approach the ewe safely, that I was holding her for him, and then he came up close, and began sniffing her all over with a sort of timid curiosity.

Quickly there was a change. It must have been a kind of revelation to Toby. In that instant he seemed to become aware of his own blood. His sniffing grew intense, audible, almost

59

fierce. He let his curiosity loose and smelled over every part he could reach of the petrified ewe. At last he sniffed too close, and the ewe began kicking out her hind legs violently and twisting her head. As easily as I could, I let her go. Toby stood back quickly, but as the ewe went through the fence and leapt away with the stiff-legged half-paralyzed bounds that showed her fear, Toby looked after her, his body taut, his eye sharply fixed on the fleeing animal.

That was the beginning of Toby's interest in sheep. It was only later that I realized what a poor way I had chosen to get him started. That came out clearly one afternoon when I was walking in the direction of Sweeney's, chatting with Jimmy Burke, who was on his way there to help the Sweeneys thatch their house. Suddenly, when we had gone several hundred yards along the road, Jimmy turned and looked below the road into the bog.

'Your dog's away,' he said.

I looked down to where Toby should have been at my heels. I had been taken by surprise. Toby had been following at my feet, as I had trained him to do, and I had no idea that he was no longer there. Jimmy pointed him out a good eighty yards to the south of us, barking at a sheep he had cornered against a bank of turf. Then occurred a crucial moment in Toby's training as a sheep dog, as I realized later. At the time, I still knew too little about dogs to appreciate the moment.

'Get hold of him good,' Jimmy said, 'and beat him well.'

'The dog's been hit too much already,' I said, thinking of the slaps Toby had had for much slighter misbehaviour.

'I'm telling you, get well hold of that dog and beat him well. Once he takes that way of doing, he'll not stop more. He'll go always after one sheep and be no good to you as a dog.'

Then he offered to hit the dog for me—really it was to be a punch with one of his large and powerful fists against the dog's head. He had told me before of punishing dogs that had jumped at visitors to his house. 'I hit them just that once, and they never try that again.'

Still I refused to let him hit Toby, and I did not do it myself. But Jimmy's warning was right. I had made a crucial mistake in the dog's training. As I started working sheep with Toby—and he could 'cap' them well enough when he wanted to, for he was fast and alert—there usually came a moment when he picked out one ewe, separated her from the flock, and chased her down the hill until, finally, the ewe would drop down terrified, and freeze to the ground. Then Toby would stand over her, his long tongue out, panting, or else barking fiercely. I could find no way of breaking him of the habit. I tried slapping him, or shaking him, then punching him, and always remembered Jimmy's advice to follow up the blows with petting—'coaxing' he called it—and then starting right out again after the sheep. Then Toby would behave well for a while, but as soon as the sheep had been brought together into a group he began showing signs of wanting to molest them. My warnings to him to stay away from the sheep only seemed to sharpen his ferocity, and before many seconds he would tear one of the ewes out of the flock—I say 'tear' literally, because he would take hold of some bit of her fleece with his teeth and separate her from the rest—and then chase her hundreds of yards off. And he was shrewd enough in his way of doing it. After the first few times, he always saw to it that both he and the ewe went out of sight over the nearest brow of hill, and by the time I had come up to where I hoped to catch sight of them, Toby, at least, and sometimes both of them, had disappeared.

Then would follow a long, hard search for the dog. My whistling and calling were useless, as always in the past, and Toby's way was to lie low for a while, then make a wide circle around me and back home, where I would find him lying in his house as, wet with sweat, out of breath and—I seem to remember—stooped with fatigue, I would get back in despair wondering where the dog was.

By then it would seem pointless to hit him. He would not understand why. As I see now, that was underestimating his intelligence. Yet the feeling remained that I should be able to win him and train him with kindness, not blows.

'Let the dog work the sheep,' was the advice of Black Jimmy of Suhill. Black Jimmy was the oldest man around, tall, thin, and very old—some said over ninety—but his hair and thick eyebrows were still the deep black that had given him his nickname, and he was still on his feet and farming sheep.

'Talk to him. He'll understand every word you say.' Black Jimmy shook his head emphatically and drew out the words when he said 'every word'. 'If he gets in too close, tell him to stay back. "Stay back! Stay back!" ' he called in illustration.

No one would endorse the idea of hitting the dog.

'Not at all,' Wee Brogan said. 'The dog's wild for work. Give him plenty of work and you'll soon see a good dog.' Wee Brogan was a dwarf, and had never worked sheep in his life. His tiny legs would not have carried him over the hills very rapidly. But his full-size torso was all the more powerful for his shortness of stature, and he was the workhorse of the region, capable of carrying loads that would have put normal men down. And when he wasn't working, he was observing, building up storehouses of knowledge about men and animals. 'I often seen dogs like that, a wee bit wild at the start, you know. Plenty of work, and they turned out fine in the rear.'

But Old Boyle, two miles down the country on the flat land below the hills, remarked, 'There's no man up there can train a dog except Jimmy, you'll have to follow his advice.' And as time went on, it seemed there was no way of doing otherwise. The dog had to be punished to the point where he would obey, and that evidently meant hurting him.

One day I was gathering the ewes to put them in a fenced field. It was November, when the ram was put out, and I wanted all the ewes together in a small space so that the ram would not have to go wandering about hunting for the ones that were in heat. For the next six or eight weeks I would be gathering them every day, and there would be plenty of work for the dog. It was the ideal time to train him. We were bringing in a group of ewes, and I was hoping all would go well. As we neared the park one of them bolted away from the rest. Toby tore out, capped the ewe, and put her back with the others. He stopped, and looked at the flock. I could see his pink tongue partly out of his half-opened mouth, and as I whistled for him he started around the flock towards me. Then suddenly he whirled about and ran in on the flock barking fiercely.

This was the moment to punish him, to break him of the habit. I rushed into the flock myself, the sheep scattering wildly in all directions. Toby was taken by surprise. Probably he had expected me only to call to him angrily, as I usually did at such times. In his surprise, he dropped back from the ewe he was tormenting as I approached, and began to run in a large, cringing circle in the tall rushes and overgrown red grass of the old meadow. He could easily have run away from me even then, but surprise held him back, and fear. I was reminded of the first time I had seen the dog, cringing, looking for a friendly master. I knelt down and took a strong hold of his skin behind the neck. Toby cringed even lower and froze. Quickly I dropped my stick to the ground and took hold of it at the bottom, so that the thick, heavy handle was away from me, and raised it above my head and back.

Then something I did not expect happened. As the dog cringed beneath my grip waiting for the blow, and I tautened the muscles of my arm to bring the stick forward, the stick refused to move. We remained there, the two of us, caught for an instant without moving, the dog cowering, I waiting for my stick to swing forward under the pressure I was putting on it. My puzzlement lasted only an instant, and I did not have to look back to know that the curved handle of the stick had caught in the heavy rushes behind me. For a moment I wondered whether it was a sign, an indication that I should change my mind.

Quickly I freed the stick with a twist and brought it down heavily on the dog's body. As Toby felt the blow he tried to leap away, and his teeth flashed in an involuntary snarl, his head turning back towards my hand and his jaws snapping. Again I raised the stick, and brought it down on him, and a third time, putting my strength into the blows, so that the dog screamed in pain each time, twisting violently to get away from me. Then I shook the stick ominously in front of him.

Letting him go after a few seconds, I called him in behind me. Toby came in to heel and followed submissively as I walked. Now there was all the work of gathering to do again. As we went down the hill again towards the glistening marsh of the curragh, I seethed inwardly and was ready to punish the dog another time as cruelly as I had just done, even for the slightest offence. Now, I knew, I would have to watch him closely.

Carefully we rounded up the sheep. Toby, it seemed, hardly dared to get near them, pausing as soon as they started to move, looking back inquiringly at me. But I was cautious: thirty yards, forty perhaps, was the furthest I would let him away from me. After each move I called him back into heel. Quickly we brought the sheep together, up the hill to the road and up the road towards the enclosed pasture land. A group of sheep were on the rough hill ground above the pasture, and I decided to let the two groups merge, and then bring the whole flock in together.

At the pasture the sheep paused expectantly. The gate was closed, and one of the leaders turned away and started for the hill. Toby, only a few feet from me, turned to look up at me questioningly. I wondered if it was a sign that he was ready to work to my directions at last. I had never seen him do it before. I waited, watching the white fleeces bounding up the steep, short step from the road to the hill, and then the two separate groups of sheep joining into a single flock, mingling and grazing in among each other on the purple-brown heather, facing uphill and taking each individually a step or two after every mouthful of grass. They were about a hundred yards above us and I thought it was time to find out if Toby would work as he should. It would be my last attempt.

The dog was still watching me as I raised my left hand and gestured him out to the left. Quickly he dashed up the road past the sheep and bounded on to the rough hill and upward beyond where they were grazing. Losing sight of him as he ran beyond the flock I held my breath. For a minute nothing seemed to happen. Then I saw the highest sheep lift their heads and turn. Toby came into sight just beyond them and paused, looking towards me. I moved up the road to a point where I could see better what he would do and motioned him back around the sheep in the other direction. Toby turned and made a broad arc behind the sheep, running slowly and easily. As he passed each sheep he hesitated for just a second until the sheep lifted her head and turned away from him. Hearing me again the dog stopped and waited for another signal. Quickly moving down in front of the sheep and below them I motioned Toby out behind them another time. I noticed that someone had appeared on the road at the crest of the hill and was watching our manoeuvres. Now, I wondered, will Toby make a fool of me? The dog swept out again in a long easy arc that brought the sheep quietly into a dense mass, facing towards me. I signalled him to stay back and slowly I backed off towards the park gate, Toby all the while making slow half circles behind the sheep, keeping them together and moving them gradually towards me as I backed away. Opening the gate I stepped aside and watched the sheep file through it and away into the pasture, sniffing and nibbling the fresh grass, three weeks ungrazed, as they went. Toby came to my foot and stopped just as Jimmy Burke arrived from the road. It was him I had noticed on the crest of the hill.

'Your dog is working,' he said.

'Yes,' I said, 'he's working.'

'Toby, Toby,' he called to the dog. Then he added, 'You have a good dog now.'

*

So Toby began to work, and for over a year he gathered the sheep for me. Not without faults, it is true, but with good qualities too. Oddly enough whenever another farmer was in sight Toby worked better than ever. He never let me down at such times. And he worked well enough at other times too, sometimes spectacularly well, though there were moments when his old wildness would come back. I never knew when it would be, but it always meant more work for me.

After a while I learned to recognize what I thought of as a 'foxy' look the dog would sometimes get and which was a certain sign of trouble ahead. The good feeding Toby was used to left little further room for winning his loyalty that way. Gradually, in fact, I realized that Toby's loyalty would never be won. The dog would never lose his outlaw streak. He seemed to have learned too well, in those first hard six months of life, that men were not to be trusted. His resentment, or perhaps it was just some wild individuality in his blood, was taken out on the sheep. He had learned that he could no longer attack them outright but he had a shrewd way of letting them disappear over a shoulder or brow of a hill before capping them out of range of my sight. Then, as I could always tell when the sheep reappeared, Toby gave vent, out of my sight, to as much nastiness as he could short of actual crime.

Yet he had his magnificent moments too. He stayed with me through pounding rain and thunder storms when other dogs, I knew, would leave their masters' feet and run for home and shelter; and once I took him out in a snowstorm with drifts high enough to engulf him three times over but he pushed through them courageously, never flagging even when the wet snow formed into nagging lumps of ice at the ends of his thick fur. And when he wanted to he could be incredibly shrewd in handling sheep—especially, as I noticed, when someone besides myself was looking on.

There were many indications of that kind of shrewdness. I caught enough of them to make me think I was missing many more. One day Joe Diermot came over to my place looking for two of his sheep that always grazed my land. That day they were on the hill beyond the house and he asked me to bring them in with my dog. Joe had no dog of his own because he was working in Coventry and only came home twice every year, in the spring and autumn, to look over his flock and make a few repairs to his house. I called Toby and we went up the road in the direction of the two sheep, which were grazing quietly below the road, uphill from the house and on the side of the farm away from Joe's place but below the road and on the downhill slope that descended several hundred yards to the curragh. When we were about thirty yards from the sheep Joe asked me to put out the dog. Since we wanted to send the sheep back towards Joe's we were both thinking that the dog should go up the road to the right of and past the sheep and then turn left beyond them, so cutting them off and herding them back towards my house and down the road past it to Joe's. I raised my right hand and snapped my fingers in the direction of the road, expecting Toby to follow the uphill signal. Instead Toby suddenly ran off the road and down to the left, at full speed, below the sheep and between them and the house and turning them away from it.

Joe cried out in alarm. 'He's going the wrong way! Call him in!'

I didn't know what Toby was up to but it was too late to change his approach then. I knew his speed and I thought he would bring the sheep to us in the end, so I let him go.

'Call him in!' Joe cried out again.

Toby bounded downhill until he was well below the sheep and then stopped. For an instant the sheep hesitated in fear, then turned and started uphill.

'Call your dog in!' Joe implored. 'He's chasing them the wrong way.'

But in that moment Toby was beyond the sheep and heading them back up to the road. Then, as they reached the road, the sheep hesitated again. Now Toby was beyond and above them, blocking their way uphill, and the sheep suddenly dashed past us down the road, past my house, and off in the direction of Joe's farm. I called Toby back from the pursuit.

Joe was jubilant. 'By God,' he said excitedly, 'that's a great dog.'

As I thought about the way Toby had ignored my signal and how he had worked the sheep, remembering the other times he had handled these same two sheep, I finally thought I understood why he had gone out left instead of right. Toby was a fast dog, but on the downhill slope the sheep, with their much longer legs, could leap and bound faster than he could, and so outrun him. But going uphill their weight was against them and Toby, trim and light, could overtake them and so control them. Toby knew that if he went out above the sheep the way I wanted him to they would race madly downhill to the curragh before he could stop them; and I remembered how that had happened the first time we had tried to cap these same two sheep and had made just the mistake I wanted to repeat this time. But though I had not learned Toby had and would not make the same mistake again. And so he went below the sheep and forced them to do what he wanted. And the funny thing is, he knew just where he wanted to put them.

So Toby made a reputation for himself and when I went into town or to a sheep fair or mart farmers would often say to me, 'I hear you've got a good dog. Hard to get a good dog now.' And Toby did have one genuine and pure good point. If he sometimes let me down when I was gathering sheep in from the hill he never failed when it came to putting the sheep into a small yard or enclosure when we wanted to dose or dip them. His perfection and reliability at such times made up for all his faults on the hill. Once the sheep were brought together in a dense lump Toby, working close in under my eye and hand, would hold them tightly together at the gate until, sooner or later, the leaders would turn and take the only direction open to them—in, in to the yard. Jimmy Burke saw this strong point in Toby as clearly as I did. 'I never see a better dog for putting sheep in. He wouldn't let one away,' he said.

I agreed. 'They certainly go in when he wants them to.'

'It's because they know they have to,' Jimmy said. 'They know they have to go in, for he won't let any go. He wouldn't let one away.'

In my own mind though I sometimes thought Toby was more trouble than he was worth. Out gathering on the hill I could never tell when he would leave a ewe behind or send her away wild so that I could not bring her in at all that day, and sometimes he simply refused to go out for groups of sheep that were in rough or wet ground, turning his head at such times in every direction but the one I was indicating to him and putting on an elaborate mimic pretence of looking for sheep everywhere but where they really were. And worst of all, if I made him go out at such times he would usually pick out another group of sheep and race after them and raise hell with them until I overtook him. I began to realize that he was making more work for me than he was saving.

The solution, I thought, would be a second dog for gathering, saving Toby for 'putting in'. As soon as I could I found another pup, a black and white bitch, brought her up to the farm as soon as she was weaned and set out to win her loyalty from the start. My idea was to leave Toby on his chain when I went out to gather sheep, taking the bitch with me instead. Neither dog fell in with my plan. As soon as the bitch showed signs of starting to work Toby became enormously jealous and would howl unintermittently from in front of his house at the very limit of his chain. Conversely whenever I tied up the bitch and took Toby the bitch would send out piercing high-pitched shrieks that I could hear even on the neighbouring farms and that made Toby wilder than ever. It was clear, if I was to train the bitch, Toby had to be sold.

I had heard that Paddy Sweeney was looking for a dog. Unkind tales filtered through of his inability to train them himself, of his frustration trying to put sheep into his yard. His dogs would bring them down from the hill and to the yard, to the very gate, and then let them away. The sheep had learned to be wildly headstrong, turning at the gate and bucking madly past dogs and men. Paddy Sweeney, it seemed, would hardly pass up a chance at a dog with Toby's reputation. And the great thing was that he had a big scope of wild hill, a place that promised to tire Toby down to the point where he might lose his wildness as I could never take it out of him.

On a bright late spring day I started off down the road with Toby at my heel. It was rare for me to take him off the farm, and he sensed that something was up. I had to hope he would be on his good behaviour if Paddy showed any interest. I also hoped that Paddy would be standing somewhere in sight when we passed his place, but luck was against me there and I had to go all the way to the door myself. Paddy was an old sheep farmer, far too old to show any least sign of interest in the dog, but he knew too that I hadn't just stopped in for tea. Finally he asked whether I was looking for a stray sheep.

'I heard Old Boyle wants a trained dog,' I said, 'and thought this one might do him.'

Paddy's eyes darkened. He could not hide his thoughts any longer. We began to bargain.

'But will he work for me?' Paddy asked.

I let Toby go from my foot and he went over to Paddy with all his usual friendly manner to strangers and sat down before him where Paddy could get the full effect of his fine head and gleaming white breast.

'You can try him,' I said.

Outside Paddy pointed to two young sheep grazing on a near slope.

'Will he bring those two sheep up to the house?'

'Send him out,' I suggested.

Paddy raised his hand and Toby dashed out. My heart sank as I saw him go off at a tangent, ignoring the two sheep. But it was only for a moment. Further down the hill, almost hidden beyond the brow, an old ewe was grazing. Toby capped her and put her together with the two young ones and headed them all uphill towards the house. As they crossed before us I raised my hand and growled to Toby to sit, and to my relief he did. It was not the time to be casual, and I called him in as sternly as I knew how. Toby turned and came to me and crouched obediently at my foot.

It was a magnificent performance. Toby must have been as anxious to be sold as I was to sell him. Paddy could not have been more impressed and I asked the highest price I had ever heard of a dog bringing in the hills—fifteen pounds. Paddy insisted on ten bob of 'luck money' back, and I gave in to that, wanting to close the deal before Toby changed his mind and his manners. But I also gave Paddy two weeks to try the dog out.

'The money will be in a tea-cup for two weeks. If you don't like the dog, just bring him back,' I said.

I held my breath as the fourteenth day approached. The farm had been remarkably tranquil without Toby's howling. Toby must have had an idea what the arrangement was too because he never started his wild tricks again until the trial period was over. Stories came back of Paddy and Toby working beautifully together. Someone even told me that Paddy was 'a great trainer of a dog'. And even when Toby's wildness flashed through Paddy told me he would never part with him.

'The dog will die on the farm,' he said.

For me the great satisfaction was in hearing other farmers talk about Toby putting the sheep into Paddy's yard and how he 'would never let one away.'

The Resurrection of the Donkey

Willy found the donkey eyeless, his hooves awkward above his white belly, his jaws askew in a final grimace. The carcass lay on a slope. When the donkey had tumbled and couldn't right himself, the hooded crows had pecked out his eyes and he had died during the night.

'Go down for Eamon,' Willy told his wife. 'The donkey's dead on the hill. Tell him to bring his own spade. He'll only break mine if I let him use it.' And he went to the byre to milk the cows.

Eamon was so used to being called on to bury dead animals that, though he hated the job, he never thought to refuse. He was just finishing his morning tea when Willy Ward's wife came for him, and he decided to go at once. It was Saturday and he wanted the afternoon free for Gallagher's pub. He got his spade from the shed, and they went up the road together. Eamon's dog followed him for a hundred yards or so, until Eamon growled at him to go home, and he did.

All he had heard from Mrs Ward was that the donkey was 'dead on the hill.' She gestured in the direction of the High Rock as they got to the house, realizing as she did so that Willy hadn't actually told her which part of the hill the donkey had died on. Even so, she didn't tell that to Eamon. It was better to have him set off and find the donkey himself than give him cause for delay.

'The hill' was about a square mile of land behind the Ward house. It was covered with heather and hard coarse grass, and was good for grazing sheep, or for cattle in the summer. It took Eamon more than an hour to find the donkey, but it didn't occur to him to give up, go back to the house, and get instructions from Willy. He just kept looking until he found it.

When Willy came back, he and his wife discussed the matter and realized that Eamon would have trouble finding the donkey, which wasn't anywhere near the High Rock but over at the Round Spring. Neither thought it mattered if Eamon lost time looking for the donkey. 'Two shillings is what he gets for the job—nothing more. The time is his own,' Willy stated. They agreed that Eamon was too simple-minded to care how he used his time.

When Eamon finally found the donkey, he carefully sized up the dead body to see how long, wide and deep the grave would have to be. He decided to dig just downhill from the body so that he could lever it in with his spade instead of having to go down for help when he was finished digging. He tested the spot for depth, driving his thin spade all the way to the handle in the soft, moist bog. Satisfied with the depth, he carefully marked out a plot about thirty inches wide by four feet long, cutting the heavy grass and heather with the tip of his spade in perfectly regular lines. Then he stood back and checked the dimensions against the donkey, making sure of the fit. After that he cut the area within the lines into neat small squares and skinned the grass off in sods about three inches thick and the size of kitchen floor tiles. These sods he carefully piled to one side. After that he began methodically cutting the underlying soft turf in neat bricks, piling them on the side of the pit away from the donkey.

When he had cut to a depth of three feet it suddenly occurred to him to look at the donkey again. He wondered if it had moved. Climbing from the pit, he examined it. He was sure it had not moved. What had caught his eye was the movement of the long winter fur in the breeze, or possibly a sheep grazing higher up the hill.

Back in the pit the feeling took hold of him again that the donkey might have moved after all. He placed himself so that he could watch the donkey as he worked, thinking that if the body started to roll while he was in the pit, it could fall right on him.

Someone more particular about his time, or less simple-minded than Eamon, might have dug to three or four feet and let it go at that. The donkey was a large one, but all that was necessary was to get a thin covering of earth over him, was the way anyone else would have reasoned. But as Mrs Ward had said, Eamon didn't know how to value his time. The day was dry, the bog was soft and easy to dig, and so he meant to make the grave a proper depth. Besides, he noticed that the donkey's legs had stiffened during the night and might stick up through the sod covering if the body was not buried far enough down.

He had reached a depth of four feet when again he had the feeling that the donkey had moved. Climbing out of the pit, he once more looked the carcass over carefully. Nothing about it had changed. The empty sockets, in which the first flies had begun to crawl, the twisted grimace of the jaws, the uncoordinated extension of the legs, all were as they had been when he started work. Then he noticed that the soft upper wall of the pit had bulged very slightly under the dead animal's weight. Another foot down would be enough, he decided. Further than that might not be safe. He measured the pit with the handle of the spade to see how deep it already was.

Looking apprehensively from time to time at the large carcass, Eamon continued his work, methodically and neatly cutting out the final depth of brick-like chunks of bog. He was about two-thirds finished when, without thinking, he looked up suddenly. The donkey was moving. Putting up a hand to shield himself, he dodged out of the way of a foreleg.

In the next instant he blacked out. He was not conscious of the donkey's body coming down on him. But the blackout only lasted for a part of an instant, and he was aware of falling

74

back into the soft ground at the bottom of the pit. The donkey must have fallen against him and crushed the breath out of him. He gasped frantically for air. Then he realized that that was an illusion. The donkey hadn't actually touched his chest at all. On falling towards the pit it had rolled over, and the four hooves had fallen first. The stiff legs had entered the pit, sustaining the body, which—so nicely had Eamon estimated the size of the corpse and the dimensions of the grave—barely wedged itself into the pit and rested again on its own four legs, just as it had done in life.

Eamon found himself on his back, alive, unharmed, but pinned, his knees bent and awkwardly raised, his cramped legs apart under the dead donkey, face to face with the donkey almost, except for the fact that the donkey's head had been caught by the wall of the pit and kept up by it. Light filtered down around the donkey's shoulders and tail, and Eamon could see that he had two or three inches of space in which to live and breathe. He felt the donkey's four hooves against the sides of his ribs and thighs, and understood that only their stiffness was keeping the weight of the body off him.

Quickly seeing that he was trapped, he knew that he must lie as still as possible and wait for help. If he moved, he would risk bringing the full crushing force of the carcass down upon himself. It would soon be time for Mrs Ward to send Willy up with tea for him, or bring it herself. Having reached that decision, he had no further thoughts, but concentrated instead on hoping that the donkey would not settle any further. 'They'll soon come,' he told himself from time to time.

But Willy and his wife had no intention of bringing tea to Eamon. 'That simple-minded fool must still be wandering about looking for the donkey,' Willy told his wife. 'Wonder he wouldn't have it buried by now and be down for tea.' And they put Eamon out of their thoughts.

In the pit, trapped under the donkey, Eamon lay quietly and waited for help. In the sky above he could hear the two hooded crows that had removed the donkey's eyes calling to each other. It was a sound he knew well, a sound like two little glass perfume bottles clinking dully together with a hollow noise that carried strangely far. It was an ominous sound, for he knew it meant some animal was down and helpless. He wondered whether it was a ewe, or perhaps a lamb.

Again he heard the sound, the dull, hollow knocking together of the little bottles, and then suddenly he heard his own stomach answering with hollow, gurgling noises from the gut. 'It must soon be time for tea,' he thought.

Lying there in the soft pit with no other resort but quietness, Eamon's eyes grew accustomed to the light and, involuntarily, he began to examine the parts of the donkey he could see, the underparts. As he did so he wished he had not, but once started he could not stop. First he noticed that the donkey's legs had stiffened even more, so that the space between him and the donkey had widened slightly. Instead of being encouraged by that, however, it made him think that things could also go the other way.

As he pondered that, he noticed another change that made him uneasy. The donkey's penis, which had been completely withdrawn into its stomach, its presence revealed only by a circle of tightly puckered black skin, now began slowly and stiffly to emerge. It had an oddly menacing quality. It was as if the donkey were coming to life again. And as he thought that, he could just see a movement of the donkey's tail stiffening backward away from him. He heard the plop of clods of manure falling about his feet. At that moment, the donkey's head loosened and shifted downwards, the long heavy teeth of its grimacing jaw and the eyeless sockets coming to rest just over his own head in a grotesque grin.

Eamon kept cool. 'It will soon be tea-time,' he told himself, though he knew that tea-time had long passed. 'Best to keep still,' he repeated to himself. He heard another clod of donkey-manure plop into the soft turf and involuntarily watched the stiff organ protruding over further towards him. 'It will soon be tea-time.'

Willy and his wife had not forgotten about Eamon. 'Wonder that simple-minded idiot isn't done yet,' Willy said again. 'It's his own time. Two shillings is all he gets, if he takes all night.'

Later in the afternoon, when the sun was low, Mrs Ward hanging up the laundry heard the hollow sound of the two crows, paused to look up the hill towards them, and remembered about Eamon. 'Willy,' she called, 'you wouldn't go up the hill to see about Eamon?'

Willy was milking the cows. 'He's long since done and gone to Gallagher's pub. He does every Saturday afternoon. Nothing would keep him out of it.'

The same opinion was held independently at Eamon's home. Even his mother didn't give his absence much thought. She had learned to contain her fears over her absent sons.

As darkness came on, Eamon knew that no one was coming to look for him. The donkey's manure lay in a heavy heap on his cramped feet, the long protruding organ pressed into his gut, the grim staring jaws were within an inch of his nose, and the empty eye-sockets remained brilliantly impressed on his mind even after it was too dark to see anything. A light drizzle started, and after a while Eamon felt the drops of moisture running off the donkey's head and on to his own.

It was only when Eamon's brother Seamus got back from Gallagher's pub at 3 a.m. that it was realized at home that Eamon was lost. Seamus and another brother, Patsy, took a light and went up to Willy Ward's to ask. At 3.30 Willy and his wife had only been in bed for an hour. As soon as Willy heard about Eamon's absence he dressed, took a light, and went up the hill with Eamon's two brothers. They gasped uneasily when they found the pit with the donkey upright in it, the shaft of the spade sticking ominously upward out of it.

'Eamon,' Patsy called.

'Yes, Patsy?' Eamon replied quietly.

'What happened?' Patsy asked.

'The donkey come to life again,' Eamon answered.

77

It was dawn before they got Eamon out. Fearing to shift the donkey by themselves, they got three more men and some ropes and did it the safe way. Eamon came out unharmed. They watched him as they drew him up, expecting him to start babbling hysterically or madly about the experience, but Eamon said nothing at all. He was oddly silent. Only when he reached home did he say anything at all, and that was: 'Is the kettle on?'

Eamon's experience was the favourite conversation topic for months afterwards. 'Isn't it odd too,' the schoolmaster commented, discussing it with the priest, 'that he kept his head and stayed so cool in that unnerving position?'

'Yes,' replied the priest, a reddish-blond softly smiling man with a melodious voice. 'That's the marvellous thing *about* it. Anyone else would go mad, I'm thinking, but Eamon was just too simple-minded to. That's what saved him.'

Joe's Return

For Joe it was a return to the time of his youth. When he had left forty years before he had known he would return one day, and now that time had come. It was clear he was not returning to Tullynabaha an old man in his own mind. He was restoring an interrupted connection, resuming a way of life he had left in his early thirties and he thought of himself as he was then. He bought a bicycle and cycled the four miles to the nearest tiny country shop—the 'Barristers' he called it, to my confusion, for Joe had a legalistic streak and had often taken his neighbours to court when their animals spent too much time on his land—or the five miles to the Letterbarrow Post Office general store, or the eight miles to Mountcharles, or the ten to Donegal Town. He lived on a rigorous, almost military schedule: up at 6.30, work until 2, the rest of the day off. He set a large garden of potatoes and cabbages, piped running water to his house from a spring hundreds of yards up the hill, re-roofed and thatched the dilapidated sheds, had a year's supply of turf won and gathered when few others had even started cutting, threw down copious areas of concrete pavement around the outside of his house, and every morning early was out rounding up his sheep and every evening late. He was the first to dose, shear, dip. He bought in sixty strange ewes and quickly put up fences on his hill ground to hold them in. He spread two tons of slag on his fields by hand and waited eagerly, impatiently, to see the hoped-for improvement in the meadow grass.

Through it all he was like a young man. I ran into him one day in town magnificently dressed in a neat, well-tailored black suit, wearing a handsome new hat and a new, perfectly knotted tie. He seemed particularly happy and invited me for a drink in the local hotel bar. His wife had won a law-suit over some inherited land and the decision meant seven or eight hundred pounds for them. It seemed like the crowning bit of good luck. Forty years of hard work to reach the pension, taking in boarders to help build up their savings, and now, with all their children grown up and well-employed, Joe had come to live in his old house and set up his old farm again, the place where he was born, and the judge's decision seemed to ratify the rightness of all he had done. We had a few drinks and Joe told me he was sixty-nine. It was *a propos* of a remark I made that Condy Gallagher, who had sheared our sheep that summer, was sixty-seven and could still work harder than most young men. Joe pulled himself up even straighter than usual.

'I'm sixty-nine,' he smiled, 'and I'm as fit as a fiddle!'

He held himself almost at attention, as if inviting examination. It was true. I had found it hard to believe that he was in his sixties, harder yet that he was at the end of them.

It was that inner attitude that was most interesting to me, Joe's crisp negation of the forty intervening years—the lost years. Not in words. His only reference to them was when, as happened often, he would tell me that someone in the city had doubted how long he would stay in the rough discomfort of the Irish hills after so many years of city convenience. 'I've looked at the old brick walls too long,' would be his reply. Then he would look at me for emphasis and repeat, this time not to his imaginary interlocutor but to me, 'I looked at those old walls too long.'

Gradually I realized how empty those years must have been for him. His mind was always with the farm—the house, the sheep, the hills. It was remarkable to me how he had planned things. He had realized in the 1930s that there was no living to be made in Donegal and when his parents died and he had nothing more to keep him on the farm he decided to leave and find a job in Scotland. Before he left he built a new house, quarrying the stone only feet from the site, planning rooms and hearths and ground plan on an ample scale, far grander than the cramped proportions of the other mountain houses, than any house around, and roofing it with slate, a roof that would last his lifetime without care, unlike the rough green thatch of rushes which, on other houses, had to be renewed every two or three years. Joe's house was built to last and it was built with proportions, high ceilings, spacious rooms, broad hearths, that would befit his victorious return from the city. He had two workmen to help him with the building of the house and when he had finished he was £40 in debt. 'That was a lot of money in those days,' he told me. It must have been, I know, for it was the price of six or seven milk cows then.

So he went off, first to Scotland, later to Coventry and within a year he had paid off his debt and was free. He worked in factories mostly and held his last job for thirty years. He bought a house in Coventry, his wife let rooms, the children grew up serious and sober. Every year that he could manage it Joe returned for two weeks, or three, whatever his vacation was, to repair the roof, to look at his sheep, to dip, perhaps, or shear them if it was the right time of the year, and to sell the wool and the surplus lambs. It gave him enormous pleasure when he returned to his job at the factory to be able to talk about his 'place' and his sheep, how they had paid for his trip there and back and left a profit over. The flock suffered while he was away. Though there was always someone looking after the bare essentials, every year some sheep were lost for lack of constant shepherding. But the flock and the house were Joe's connection with his land. They were the reality that gave him distance from the 'old factory walls' that he endured to look at for so long. Forty years! Going away for forty years and building a grand new house just before departing—what a remarkable piece of foresight it had been.

Now Joe was back, restoring the connection with his youth. I noticed that he always wore a clean shirt and a neatly knotted tie even at farm work. When he was digging his garden or vaccinating sheep he would be wearing the brown overalls he had worn in the factories, but at any cleaner job he would wear clothes that would have been presentable in town. I remember him building Nohar Peadar's haystack, on the highest farm in the hills, hundreds of yards from any road or power line, standing high on the growing stack, dapper and clean in his fresh white shirt and neat dark tie. I was forking the hay and somehow as the stack grew gradually to the proportions of a small house and Joe's figure rose steadily higher against the clear blue sky the contrast to the rest of us became ever sharper, with our old clothes, baggy, patched, dusty with barnyard dust. So when I talk of Joe's negation of the forty years in the city I am only partly accurate. When he came back home he deliberately kept the marks of that other experience that set him off a little, raised him above the people he was born with. I thought of it as his 'education'. Yet though Joe was conscious of the difference he never showed it in words. In fact he began using the oddest old pieces of the Donegal vocabulary, long discarded by all but the oldest people of the hills. 'Forenenst,' meaning 'across from,' was one he particularly liked. But when he had been around for a while his speech returned to normal.

The fact that his flock had survived even without Joe around to watch them—there was even a time when he missed getting home for three years running—was a piece of luck that grew straight out of Joe's character, luck he made for himself without knowing at all, at the time, what he was doing. It was about a year or two before his leaving for Scotland. Three miles across the hill Nohar Peadar More was home from his twenty years hired out as a farm-hand, newly in possession of a farm so run down and a house and buildings so dilapidated that not one of his seventeen brothers or sisters would have them, even for the asking. He was over his head in work, cleaning out, repairing, rethatching, mending fences, opening clogged drains, and he had missed putting in his 'crop', the essential crop of potatoes—'pra'ys' he called them—that were his staple food and main source of energy throughout the year. To miss having the 'crop' on a farm that could not possibly earn anything that year would be a disaster but Nohar, when he woke up to the lateness of the season—it was the middle of May—found that he had been away too long to have many friends left, and those he did have were busy at their own work. Putting in potatoes is a two-man job, but Nohar set to work with his spade, determined to do as much as he could alone. Not only was that in the days before tractors in Donegal but even now, in the mid-seventies, no tractor has ever been on Nohar's farm, cut off as it is from the road by a rocky mountain stream. He was cursing the slowness of the work to himself when, looking up, he saw Joe's slender figure coming uphill towards him from the stream he had just crossed by way of the narrow bridge of wooden slabs, his spade balanced comfortably in his right hand. The two men had worked a long day, until the last light had faded, and the next day Joe was back again and again they worked the long day. At the end of it the thirty ridges of crop were in, ready to grow.

These two days had made Joe's luck with his flock. The two men had been boys together but they had scarcely seen each other on Nohar's rare visits home for twenty years. Nohar was not sure they had seen each other at all. What impressed him was Joe's spontaneous appearance to help him when he had so little to offer in return. Of course Joe paid Nohar later for the work he did with his flock while he was away. He knew, though, that it was not the pay: absentee money doesn't buy a loyal helper, not in the hills, where every man has too much work of his own. But Nohar loved sheep anyway and loved to work with them. Sheep were important to him because he lived from them, and Joe was his friend.

But after Joe came back to settle the friendship cooled. Probably any good judge of human nature would have fore-seen that. Maybe Joe, after all those years of earning good pay in the city, didn't really respect Nohar for doing so much work with the sheep for so little pay. Nohar would sense that at once if it was so. And maybe Nohar got a little angry with Joe one warm autumn day for not showing up to help with the hay; but Nohar had too much work with hay on his tractor-less farm: even bringing the huge cocks of hay in to be built into stacks was all done with human beasts of burden. Not even a donkey was allowed, for fear of poaching the meadow, and people got impatient with Nohar and preferred to stay on their own farms and do lighter jobs, and get more done with less effort.

What finally broke them up was Winnie Jane, McGrory's only daughter, and widely reputed to be 'one of the prettiest and smartest girls ever to come out of these hills.' Winnie Jane had been born when Nohar was thirty-five and he had spotted her at once as the wife he wanted and had worked and saved and waited patiently for the time to come. The McGrorys didn't do anything to discourage the idea, for Nohar was a great worker and a good hand at everything. Over the years it was Nohar who saw to it that McGrory's house and byres were always perfectly thatched. He used to carry his long, heavy ladder that he needed for thatching three miles over the hills—McGrory never had ladders or barrows or carts or any of the other things usual on farms—then cut the rushes and carried them in himself, and always did a perfect job of thatching. He was proud to show his skill. And when there was work with sheep he was there, dipping, dosing, shearing, he was the acknowledged best hand at all that. There were two things the McGrorys could never do with sheep—it turned their stomachs: castrating lambs and inoculating them. Nohar always did those things too.

All the while he was waiting for Winnie Jane to be his wife I suppose McGrory told him softly, 'Wait a wee while, Nohar, till she's a bit older.' When Winnie Jane was twenty and Nohar fifty-five she went to visit her aunt in New York and stayed on there to be a waitress, and a good one too, it seems.

From time to time word went through the hills that a large cheque had arrived from New York to be saved towards the building of a new house. Every few years there was a visit home. At those times plenty of thatching got done. But Winnie Jane never stayed. She always went back to her job, which was always at the same restaurant.

It was only Nohar who lived so perfectly in the past. The rest of them, though they lived in the same miserable primitive conditions, in kitchens cluttered with sacks of grain and spuds and churns and creels of turf and wet sprawling sheep dogs and the sudden irruptions into the kitchen of orphan lambs that were used to being bottle-fed or irate hungry hens looking for their evening ration of corn, in rooms choked with smoke on days the wind blew down and strewn with ashes and tracked with mud at any time of the year—in spite of it all they all realized how far behind the times they were. Only Nohar still saw something glorious in the thatch house on the side of a hill, six hundred yards from the nearest stretch of road, a thousand from a power-line, four miles from a phone, thirty from a doctor. There was something incredibly modern about his total rejection of the modern world, and something incredibly ancient too. As for Winnie Jane, she never said much, but in New York she had had a taste of the future, she had seen it coming and she had no intention of protracting the Middle Ages into the twenty-first century.

It was on one of those visits that things came to a head. Nohar was getting old, he was in his mid-sixties, and he felt he could hardly wait any longer. The McGrorys had been putting him off for so many years he could hardly bring the matter up to them and he didn't know how, even if he could get to talk to Winnie Jane alone—but all conversation was always in a cramped lump of hunched bodies around the kitchen hearth, even in summertime—he didn't know how he could propose to her directly. He asked Joe to be his go-between and Joe, thinking of the years of loyal friendship and service, couldn't say no. Once he had said yes, however, he realized what a ridiculous spot he was in. He was afraid he would make himself even more ridiculous than Nohar. It was about that time I heard him grumbling about Nohar being 'a head case'.

'After all those years he watched your sheep, Joe?' I asked in slight surprise.

'Oh, you're right, you're right there,' Joe replied quickly. 'Nohar's a great man, and he'd do anything for you. He's a great man that way.'

Then he paused and poked the glowing turf on the hearth.

'But it's funny too the way he takes notions. He's got the idea of marrying the McGrory girl and I suppose they don't put him off it—for the work, you know. He's got tired of waiting now and says this is it, so he come to me the other day and asked me would I speak for him. I knew the way things are, but I could not refuse him, so I said I would.'

Joe's small blue eyes, which had never ceased being hill-farmer's eyes, small, perfect almonds, deeply embedded under the overhanging protective brows, looked at me brightly, sharply. His lean, lined face smiled broadly.

'By God, I waited a day and then when he called again after that and asked me did I speak, "I did," I said.'

'But you didn't, Joe?' I interjected, incredulous.

'Of course I didn't. Don't you know that? But I had to tell him I did. "I did," I said. "Well, what did she say?" he asked. You would think he would know better. "She said," I told him, "she says she can think of no better man than Nohar Peadar More, but for the moment she has no intention of marrying until she has enough money, which she will in a few more years of work, to see her family secure." '

Joe smiled broadly and started to laugh.

'How was that for an answer? Was it not a good one? Because it's neither yes nor no, you see, and he took it.'

I wondered why Joe hadn't simply discussed the matter of disabusing Nohar with the McGrorys and let them do it. I suppose he knew they never would and mentioning it to them would be like presenting them point blank with the reproach for their long deception of Nohar, accusing them. And he couldn't open Nohar's eyes to the facts because—well, how do you tell an old friend he's mad? Joe's solution was probably the simplest. We all knew anyway that Winnie Jane would never marry. She wasn't the type.

And that's what upset Joe's scheme. Winnie Jane had no sooner left than the McGrorys let it be known that she was engaged to a young fellow from Sligo who was also a restaurant worker in New York. Nohar took it hard. I watched him age a decade in ten days.

'The old hoor' (meaning Winnie Jane's mother, Brigid, who had never been known to have relations with anyone but Dennie, her husband) 'the old hoor knew it all the time but kep' quiet until I build their haystack and thatch it for them.'

There was something pitiful about the scaling down and concentrating of the grievance into that one contemporary haystack, for everyone knew it wasn't the haystack but all the years of work, all the years the McGrorys had relied on Nohar for so many things and used him so adroitly, scarcely having to work themselves at dangling the luring hope before him. His age made him absurd, but the work—the work! It not only entitled him to Winnie Jane but to three Winnie Janes, or Rachels or Leahs or Dinahs or Hepsibahs or whatever their names were. But this happened in the boggy Irish hills, not on the clay fields of Mesopotamia. Things are different here.

About that time Joe discovered slabs from the local saw mill. Slabs are the part of the tree the lumberman rejects, the long bark-covered first slice of the trunk, a cross between a proper board and a rough piece of bark. They cost £4 a load. The load could be anything from a donkey-cart to a lorry-full, the price was always £4. When Joe found out about the slabs he saw their possibilities at once, hired a large tractor and trailer and two men to help, and put on the highest most tightly packed load the trailer would take. When he got them home he set to work building up an enclosure for his sheep around the old stone sheds and byres he had already repaired and thatched. The long slabs, often six feet or more, were ideal for the purpose. When sheep are desperate or even merely determined it is surprising how high they can leap in a thrust for freedom. But they would not try six feet.

Joe put up the enclosure so fast he had it finished before I knew he was at work. I first saw it from the hill above his house and the cluster of neatly thatched stone sheds and byres enclosed by the stockade-like fence of rustic slabs made a striking picture. The great long bark-covered slices of larch and sycamore and oak gave the feeling almost of a frontier settlement. I suppose others got the same impression. When Amby Meehan the taxi man saw it he looked for a moment and then exclaimed softly, 'Fort Laramy!'

In midsummer Joe got word that his sister, whom everyone called simply 'the nun', was deathly ill in her convent in northern Scotland. Joe was seventy, 'the nun' eighty, and he felt he had to hurry. This would be the last time they would ever see one another. He planned to be back again in ten days and the McGrorys and I offered to keep an eye on his sheep while he was away. I was glad for the chance to do him a favour, since he had done a number for me.

Joe left. Two weeks later scribbled notes arrived on small, wrinkled pieces of cheap paper, asking us to round up his sheep for 'the punching'. He would not be back in time.

'The punching', I should explain, is the annual government counting of tails before the payment of the bounty. It is the high point of the sheep man's year, representing the biggest single lump of money he can expect to see at any one time. Bounty checks run into hundreds of pounds and form a central part of all calculations about the flock. It is not tails that get counted but ears. Every lamb and every year-old ewe has a notch punched out of the edge of its right ear. Hence the name. A lamb with one notch or a year-old ewe with two has been 'punched' and cannot be counted for the bounty again. A day is appointed for each region of the county and all the sheep have to be in and ready on the early morning of that day. Not to be ready is to lose the bounty.

The news that Joe would not be back in time for the punching was taken automatically as meaning the rest of us would do the work for him. Normally it was Nohar who did that work but, aside from the cooling off of his friendship with Joe, Nohar had slipped on his meadow while mowing—it was shortly after the news about Winnie Jane's engagement—and twisted his leg so badly he could hardly walk. Though I had my own sheep to gather and dip and sort out and have ready for the bounty men I didn't think Joe's sheep would give us too much extra work if we had three or four helping. I agreed to round up the sheep on the lower part of the farm, the flat marshy land below the road, and the McGrorys were to bring down the ones that were grazing on the hill above the road. My own sheep, and one ewe and lamb of Joe's that always grazed my land, were safely gathered into a new hill paddock of eight or nine acres. I had been working on it all spring and early summer, carrying out the larch and oak fence and straining posts and the coils of sheep wire and finally helping to get the fence put up. I say the sheep were safely gathered, but actually I knew there were still weak spots in the fence, small gaps on areas of rough heathery bog where the irregular ground had not yet been filled in with sods to bring it level with the bottom of the wire. There the sheep could slip out if they really wanted to. Like so many things in the Donegal hills, the fence was only relatively a fence.

When the day before the punching came I went out at about 5 p.m., as agreed with McGrory, to round up my share of Joe's sheep. By luck the weather, though threatening, was dry. It looked as if we would just get the two or three hours we needed before the rain started. As I made the circuit of the lower part of Joe's land along lake and marsh and rough hillocks of bog I could see the three McGrory brothers gathering sheep on the hill. As we came towards each other we let the two groups of sheep join above the road and drove them in a big flock into one of Joe's fenced areas.

I waited to see what was coming next. The McGrorys were Joe's next-door neighbours, he and they often helped each other out, so I assumed they would know how he put his sheep into the yard. There were two gates and the sheep would be used to going in one way or the other, but not both. I waited. The McGrorys waited too. The sheep were becoming restless and trying to bolt. I looked at Willy McGrory, the oldest of the brothers, and the one who always took the lead, but as I did he turned and started walking away.

'Willy,' I yelled, 'where are you going? How about putting the sheep in?'

'Time enough,' he yelled back. 'When Nohar gets here, he'll put them in.'

'Nohar? Nohar has a bad leg. He'll never manage to get over here. Come on, we'll put them in now.'

'I have my own sheep to gather'—just a hint of a whining tone—'sure, we'll do these later.'

Saying that McGrory turned and walked off followed by his two brothers. I looked at the sky bulging greyly downwards towards the ground. If we delayed long enough we would be in for a good soaking. It was typical of McGrory's hillbilly mentality, I decided, to do the job half way and then, by not finishing it, undo it. Off he went.

There was nothing for me to do but try to keep the sheep together without any more help than my own dog until they came back. The sloping hill meadow we had gathered them on to baffled the dog as much as it did me. Joe had proudly told me that he had that field entirely fenced. Now I found that it was a raggedy job of stretches of old wire, parts of which had rusted away so badly the sheep could go through it easily. There were two or three places like that. The trouble was that the sheep knew where the holes were but neither the dog nor I did. Again and again she found herself on the wrong side of the wire as the knowing sheep bolted quickly through the holes. I kept getting tangled up in lengths of wire that seemed to have no relation at all to the rest of the fence. As the first sheep bolted through the movement communicated itself to the whole flock. The sheep began to move in a mass back in the direction I had just brought them up from. If they scattered, all the work of gathering them would have to be done again. The maze of fences that baffled me and the dog so effectively were no obstacle to the knowing sheep. In the dim overcast light of the late afternoon I found myself gesturing wildly to the dog to go out in one direction while I ran frantically in the other. When she ran up I would be running down and as she started down I would find myself struggling upwards against the slope. It was an unequal fight. There were only two of us (and one of us had only two legs), there were a hundred and fifty of them. If we stopped them in one direction they dashed out in another. And they knew the ground.

In spite of that we managed to hold them fairly well, for a while. As always happens in situations like that, with my dog anyway, when the sheep saw the dog running madly back and forth on the hill, her tongue beginning to hang out with the effort, they knew she was tiring and one or the other of them made a bolt for freedom. When that happened (I remember it was a big greyish one with a large ewe-lamb) the dog made the fatal mistake of not running out wide enough to head off the two sheep and she wound up chasing them instead, racing after them and sending them away wild as she did so. I knew that no matter how hard we tried those two sheep would not come back for us again that day. At least we managed to keep the others in a loose scattered group on the hill.

I stood there holding the sheep together, feeling slightly foolish about the whole thing, under the bulging sky, getting impatient and wondering how the day would end. My dog looked as if she felt foolish too, at any rate anxious to get on with the job of driving in the sheep. There was nothing to do but wait. I was stuck, unless I wanted to let Joe down. On the other hand, I could not be sure the sheep were going to be put in anyway.

It was only half an hour after all before McGrory and his two brothers came back. They had not finished gathering their own sheep. I couldn't figure out what they had managed in only thirty minutes, but evidently they had done something with some of their sheep anyway and now were back to do something with some at any rate of Joe's sheep. As I watched them slowly padding back across the soft green wet fields I reflected that everything in the hills always seemed to take far longer than the time I calculated it would. I never counted on the delays which in that soft, mild, moist, soporific atmosphere seemed to account for most of any day's work.

'Will we put them in now?' I yelled, before the McGrorys had come near enough for the usual greeting and banter of small talk that necessarily precedes all more serious matters, even after only thirty minutes intermission. My impatience was pushing me beyond an etiquette that I felt, after all, was not really mine.

Willy's tone registered the omission very slightly as he called back across the gathered flock, 'We'll wait for Nohar.'

'Nohar?' I sensed a note of indignation in my voice getting out of control. 'Nohar will hardly be able to get here with his leg. He's not fit.'

'He's coming now,' Willy replied. 'There he is on the shoulder.'

I turned around and looked. Willy was right. A small dark figure had come over the shoulder of the hill to the west and was slowly, limpingly coming along the road. Willy could identify him but I would not have been able to, since I was used to Nohar's vigorous stride and saw nothing familiar in the low, slow-moving figure that I made out then. Even his small brown dog seemed to have a different gait.

It would normally have taken him only a few minutes to get from the shoulder to where we were. I realized impatiently that there was no calculating how long it would take this time. The sense of waiting, of attending the necessary arrival of an essential actor in this scene imposed a perfect stillness and passivity on all of us. The three McGrory brothers stood absolutely without movement, as if without any active thought or plan of their next necessary activity, without the slightest gesture or shifting of weight or change of posture to suggest impatience. Even the sheep had given up trying to move and stood all facing as they were when the three McGrorys had returned, their stillness and silence interrupted only by the occasional restless shuffling a few inches forward of an old ewe or the sudden querying bleat of one of the lambs. The stillness communicated itself even to me, I suppose, for after I had calculated that we would have to wait a good quarter of an hour for Nohar to reach us I cannot remember having any more thoughts at all, but just stood watching dully, patiently, his slow, limping advance through the landscape. No doubt our waiting was made easier by the knowledge that when he arrived he would take over and arrange everything.

But even in that we were wrong.

'How you puttin' them in?' was the first thing he said.

We looked back our surprise and he read our looks.

'Joe changed all since he come,' he said. 'I used to put them in from the house side, but I don't know how he's got them now.'

'He puts them in from the road,' someone said softly.

Nohar limped down with a limp that told the pain he was feeling every time he put his weight on the leg he had twisted. He went into the yard Joe had built up with the slabs and looked it over. It seems that Joe had not had time for a gate at the narrow end of the yard, the end near the house, but had barricaded it with a structure of slabs and odds and ends. It was closed in such a way that he clearly meant the sheep to go in through the big double gates facing the road. The wings of the gate were folded back and we got ready to shift the sheep.

Impressed as we all were by the methodical stockade-look

of the work none of us thought to check it for solidity, or to check the barricade at the far end. We took our positions around the sheep, two of the McGrorys standing on the road on either side of the big gate while the rest of us stayed on the hill to drive the sheep down. Nohar began a hissing noise he always used to encourage sheep to move, also emitting frequent soft guttural instructions as he called his dog to different positions. The sheep moved down to the bottom of the field and started to cross the road. I was astonished at how quiet they had become. They were filing through the gate two by two, in pairs, side by side, just as I had seen the animals represented in paintings going into the ark.

'Maybe it did happen that way,' I thought as I watched them.

Then I decided it must be Nohar's shrewd way of handling the sheep that did it.

'Nohar knows what he's doing,' I thought to myself. 'That must be the way they always go in, through the big double gate from the road.'

I had forgotten that the others were as ignorant of the routine as I was, Nohar included. Suddenly he remembered that he hadn't checked the far end of the yard to see if it was solid. He called out to the youngest of the McGrory brothers, Denny, to run around as fast as he could and make sure the sheep weren't getting out there. Denny, half panicked by Nohar's sudden shouted command, turned and raced away. As soon as he left his place on the road Nohar realized that there was nothing to keep the sheep from turning that way and scattering, so he shouted up to me to come down and take Denny's place.

I started down the hill. Twilight had come on and a light drizzle had started and I heard Nohar shouting at me to get on to the road as fast as I could. When I got there the sheep were already facing me. Behind them the ones that had gone into the yard were erupting out again in a complete reversal of their former mild behaviour. It seemed like an explosion. In a few seconds there were sheep everywhere. They were rushing past me in twos and threes. A wether lamb, for sheer joy at being unhemmed again—or was it excitement? —leapt high in the air over a non-existent obstacle as he passed me and the next dozen sheep behind him took the same invisible hurdle just as he had done. I ran around to the back of the house. My dog was racing ineffectually back and forth in great semi-circles, her head and neck stretched out in front of her more like a greyhound than a collie.

'Cap 'em, cap 'em,' I yelled, but the sound of my voice only set her to racing more wildly still.

Oddly enough the sheep had stopped when they reached the far side of the house and were standing perfectly still. For a moment I congratulated myself on that unexpected effect. Then I saw Nohar's small brown collie standing just at the edge of the crowd of sheep, not making any move to hold them, not threatening, not looking at them even, simply standing, almost in among them, still, her head hanging down as though in fatigue. Somehow the sheep sensed that they could go no further.

I decided to stay back there with Nohar's dog and the still sheep. Sounds of harassed shouting floated over the house from the yard and reached me in the twilight that had begun to settle over the landscape. I waited with the sheep until, after a long while, Nohar himself appeared and rounded them up again and put them back into the yard.

Then I found out what had happened. Joe had never got around to finishing the corral. At the far end, the end near the house, 'the nun's' illness had come before Joe could finish the gate. When he left to go to Scotland because she was dying he hurriedly put up the barricade there with anything he had on hand: bits of an old pony cart, slabs wedged in crosswise and at odd angles, the back of a kitchen chair, broken spade handles and two rusted out and fragmentary bicycle frames were what caught my eye first. I think there was also a large iron wheel hoop and an old rotting window.

It was an extraordinary composition. No wire or cord was used but an ingenious system of wedging the parts together so that all held tightly to each other without actually being jointed or tied. It seems that when young Denny McGrory, following Nohar's shouted commands, had run back to the gap to make sure about the soundness of this barricade, he had shaken it to test it, a spare piece had fallen away with a clatter, and the sudden noise had stampeded the sheep back through the front gate.

After Nohar put the sheep back into the yard I went back myself and found him limping around ordering the others about. His aim was to sort out the lambs and the year-olds and have each group in a separate shed, then put the ewes outside. The rest of us had thought it would be enough to put all the sheep—ewes, lambs, year-olds alike—into the yard and leave them there overnight, but Nohar insisted on having everything neatly sorted and ready for the morning. He had had a nasty taste of impatient bounty men.

The problem was where to put them. There were three big sheds but each of them was partly taken up with something Joe was storing: a pile of neatly folded fleeces, old furniture, tins of sheep dip or dose, spades, tools, and so on. Every time a shed door was opened to put in another lamb or year-old the sheep already in it would make a dash for freedom and had to be pushed back. Their wild movement would be followed by the sound of something falling, chairs tumbling, tools clattering or, when we looked again, the noiseless descent of a bale of wool from the top of a high mound of fleeces. In our mad scurry to catch the sheep there was not time to stop and put things right. We all wanted to be done with Joe's sheep and out after our own. Grabbing hold of a strong wether lamb that raced past me I dragged him to the shed reserved for lambs and shoved him in. As I opened the flimsy door of the shed a large, perfectly round, soot-black bastible pot, the kind once used for boiling up the huge quantities of home-grown potatoes that were the staple diet of men and animals, suddenly rolled out of the shed and tumbled an irregular course to the very middle of the yard, stopping at the feet of a group of bewildered and, after the night's events, easily terrified ewes. As they saw the large, unfamiliar black thing coming towards them they crushed themselves backwards in fright. Then the ones in front dashed blindly and desperately away, smashing unseeingly against a wall of slabs. Under the impact three or four slabs flew out and left a large gap. Instantly the sheep were gone.

The three McGrory brothers and Nohar stopped whatever they were doing and looked at the hole in the slab stockade. There was a quick consultation about what sheep had got out. If it was only ewes no one cared. They were to be put out anyway. But someone thought there had been a lamb with them, or that one of them had been a year-old.

Quickly they patched up the hole with that amazing deft way with odds and ends that seems so mysterious to anyone not bred to it, wedging the slabs back in horizontally and diagonally in a kind of weave, so that they pressed against each other and also against the slabs that were still standing in the stockade and so kept themselves in place. The bastible pot was wedged in at the very bottom to close an awkward gap.

Only about four or five sheep had got out. Most of the others were still in the yard. We couldn't be sure if one of the lost sheep was a lamb or a year-old—no one had really been looking. There were about a dozen more to be caught and tucked in to their appropriate sheds and we stood looking on for a moment, everyone in his own mind, I think, estimating how quickly we could get through with them when, all at once and for no reason I could detect, we all looked towards the barrier at the end of the yard.

To me it was a splendid, living art trouvé collage, a great gathering of forms and shapes and textures and rich symbolic suggestions of life lived, functions fulfilled, goals achieved or missed, and time transpired. The forgotten history of a remote hill farm seemed to be cryptically and mysteriously related in this spontaneous work of art.

And as we looked, it moved. The splendid gathering of wheels and slabs and rusting bicycle frames and rotted out bits of old donkey cart moved very slightly in all its parts. For a second it seemed to stabilize again. Then one of the bicycle frames shifted and fell away and as it did the wheel above it shook loose and slid down, then the window, and then the entire structure, as though having lost its master pin or wedge, disintegrated, crumbled in a marvellous slow sequence of intermittent collapse of its individual parts. In the narrow gap where the barricade had stood there was now only a scattered rubble of rust and rotting wood in shapes that mud and dung made instantly less recognizable than they had been a moment before.

There was nothing funny about it. As the barrier collapsed the already tormented ewes, as unfamiliar perhaps with that kind of midsummer madness as I was, panicked again and tore round the yard in a single scurrying circuit. In a moment they had collected their wits, found a leader and dashed through the unblocked gap, taking the remaining lambs and year-olds with them.

Men and dogs quickly rushed out again, this time in the deepest gloom of twilight possible short of darkness. We got all but three and put them back in the way they had gone out, through the narrow gap. When we had them in somebody reconstructed the barrier, more modestly, lower, less ambitiously and more solidly, with props front and back. We snagged out the remaining lambs and made a quick count. Three lambs were out. No one was sure about the year-old. It was almost dark. The drizzle was turning into rain. The business of Joe's sheep, that I thought would take two hours, had dragged on until night. The rain made it worse. We were all anxious to get back to our own farms.

Three lambs out, or four! We were close enough to the

count, I thought, even without the three. Joe could do without the bounty on three or four lambs. It was pretty good going that we had got the rest for him. We would call it a night, I thought.

Willy McGrory opened the big gates and started for home, his two brothers after him. Nohar called them back.

'What about them three, Willy, and the yirrol?'

Willy looked at Nohar for a second and lowered his eyes. He was still conscious of the years of letting Nohar make a fool of himself over Winnie Jane and found it hard to reply even to a question about rounding up a few sheep. I answered for him.

'It's good enough, Nohar. We've gathered enough of his sheep for him. We have our own to think about.'

Nohar stood absolutely still and looked at me and then at all of us. There was something like surprise in his face.

'Three lambs out,' I exclaimed. 'We're close enough to the count. Joe can do without three lambs. Willy's got plenty to do with his own sheep.'

I looked at the McGrorys.

'Go on, Willy,' I urged, 'go home.'

'You should've had all your sheep in and ready before this,' Nohar remarked as the McGrorys walked off, and I saw by their backs that they appreciated the import of that reproach as much as I did. It meant that Nohar, bad leg and all, had gathered and sorted his sheep before he had come to Joe's.

I looked wistfully in the direction of the hill paddock where I had gathered my sheep. Were any getting out? I wondered. How long would it take me to gather them in the morning? Through the drizzle and evening gloom I could still see the white shapes of the grazing ewes scattered across the slope of the hill.

When I looked back at Nohar his eyes were still on me, with the same look of surprise they had had before. I read the look easily. It told of the basic difference between us. At that moment I thought there was something heroic in Nohar.

I knew what he was thinking: we could let some of our own sheep go but we would have to get all of Joe's, because Joe wasn't there to do it himself. Nohar liked to do a perfect job for himself. His standards were even higher for an absent friend. His loyalty had overcome all the mocking laughter about his ill-considered proposal to Winnie Jane. What remained were the two days of spontaneous work helping to put in crop forty years before, still remembered. For Nohar belonged to the past.

But I could not bring myself to more effort. The drizzle was turning into rain. Too much of a wetting, a muscle pulled catching one of those lambs and I would be in bad shape for handling my own sheep the next day. I thought I had done enough for Joe.

All this was without words. It was only thoughts, as we stood facing each other in Joe's stockade.

Nohar's face softened.

'We've done enough,' he said. 'You have your own sheep to worry about. We'll quit now.'

I was relieved.

'I'll just close up all well here before I get some tea at McGrory's,' he added. 'You go on home.'

The next day the sheep were punched. It was only afterwards, when I went around to see Nohar that afternoon, that I found out that he hadn't gone to McGrory's for tea at all. After we all had left he made sure the yard was secure and then he and his dog Fly had gone out and rounded up the missing ewes and lambs without any help and on that leg—I winced thinking about it—he snagged the lambs and stuffed them into the right shed. The one ewe he couldn't get was the big grey one my dog had put away wild. Her lamb was the only one missing, except for the one I had had punched in with my own sheep.

As we sat by Nohar's hearth over a bottle of whiskey he grew philosophical, as usual when a high point of the farming year had been reached and passed. The hay he had been mowing when he hurt his leg had lain in the steady rain and begun to rot. We talked about the bad hay-weather and his mind went to the cycle of the seasons. There would be more hay next year, he said. This year's rotting hay would melt back into the ground and turn into next year's fresh growth, just as we would all, men and animals, return to the ground and turn into fresh life again. As he talked I was reminded of the rich green place on his meadow where he had buried a dead ewe.

A few days after the punching Joe came back. The nun was living still, had even taken a turn for the better. He had used the time in Scotland to get a new set of uppers. He was delighted about our work with the sheep. Though the bounty cheques weren't due for another month I offered to pay him right away for the lamb punched with mine.

'Time enough when the money comes,' he said.

But I was anxious to clear the debt and pulled out the three pounds for the lamb and handed it to him.

That was the end of the punching for that year. In September the bounty cheques came. I ran into Joe on the hill above my house as I was coming down from going through the sheep. He had collected a big cheque. He had even collected for the two lambs that weren't in for punching with the rest of the flock. The local administrator, knowing his reputation for honesty, and that he was away visiting the dying nun, had given him the full count. Joe was jubilant.

I thought of the three pounds I had handed over for the lamb punched at my place. Joe had collected twice on that one. I admired his jubilation and good luck too much to ask for it back. His good luck—it had grown straight out of his own character, his known reputation for straightness. It was, after all, a just reward.

Joe raised his eyes towards the sky.

'It looks like the good hay-weather has come at last,' he said.

As we stood there talking we suddenly heard the distant,

bubbling noise of a tractor floating across the face of the hills.

'It's over at McGrory's,' Joe commented. 'The first time ever they've got a man to cut hay for them with a tractor. He's to come to me in the afternoon.'

He explained eagerly how much hay could be cut and won with the use of tractors.

'The old scythe is a thing of the past,' he concluded.

As I listened to his talk I looked at the hills behind him. The broken clouds were making a pattern of the warm yellow of the sun and the deep cool blue of the shade. The green of the hills was lost in those two other colours. It would indeed be a good day for hay.

I thought of Nohar. Probably he could use a hand. As Joe went off home I got my hay-fork and started over the hill. Just over the crest of the shoulder Nohar's farm came into sight. I stopped and inspected it for signs of action but could detect no movement, no person. The few grasscocks of hay that he had tried to save from the rain were just as they had been a few days before, not shaken out at all, sitting still in the low mounds that by their lowness and flatness told me, even across the valley, that they were rotting.

I stood for a moment looking. Then, carried to me on the warm-cool autumn breeze that was blowing down from the hill and along the valley, I heard the soft sound of the stone whirring against the steel blade of a scythe, the soft rhythmical sound of the sharping of a scythe. I listened to it for a moment without being able to locate with my eyes the source of the sound. Then it stopped and in a moment I caught sight of the low, curved figure mowing a fresh section of meadow. As always before his optimism had survived and overcome the bad weather. Painful leg, rain, lack of help and all, he would win the hay as he had done for so many years, as men had done for so many generations before him. It was one more repetition in an eternity of repetitions. He faced downhill as he mowed, the scythe held out before him, moving it in large sweeping arcs, each movement a gentle rhythmic duplication of those that came before it and as he moved slowly downwards I saw the broad swathe of fresh-cut hay lengthen out, as the grass fell in heavy, even clumps before the slow, steady stroke of the scythe.

Danny's Debts

Danny Ward bent over the rabbit. The snare had caught it neatly around the neck and it had choked to death during the night. Loosening the snare Danny slipped the rabbit's head out. He took a small brown-glass bottle from his jacket pocket and unscrewed the white metal cap. Drawing back the lid of the rabbit's left eye with his thumb he tapped a few grains of white strychnine into it from the brown bottle, then repeated the process for the other eye. He glanced into the bottle to see how much of the poison was left in it, screwed the cap tightly back on and put the bottle into his pocket again. With one end of a short piece of yellow cord from the same pocket he bound the rabbit's legs together and tied the other end to the bottom of a larch fence post a few feet from where the snare had been set. As he stood up again his eye rested on the square wooden slab on which he had printed with red sheep-marking fluid the rough capitals: LAND POISONED —DANGER. He could just make out the words in the early morning twilight.

Returning the few hundred yards across his own fields to his house Danny went to the bedroom, took off his clothes and got back into bed, which was still kept warm by the heat from his wife's broad and fleshy body. He rolled towards her and at once became drowsy. As he was falling asleep he heard the rooster crow for the second time.

At eight a.m. Mary Ward heard the alarm and got out of bed. She woke their four children and got them started washing and dressing and eating their breakfast of oatmeal porridge and tea with milk and sugar, getting them ready to leave for school. Though the running water, the cold direct from the spring on the hill, the hot by way of the copper back-boiler in their turf-fired range, had been in for over two years she still thought of it as a recent improvement and enjoyed the convenience of having it every time she turned the taps and saw the water filling the basin, or pulled the black plastic stopper and watched it flow effortlessly away. The gas cooker had been there only a little longer and it was another convenience she still consciously enjoyed, especially in the mornings when cooking porridge and boiling tea was much faster than it had been when she had had to rekindle the fire and wait for the range to regain its heat. The cooker saved her twenty minutes. The electric light itself had only been in the house for the last four years. They were used to that by now, however, and seldom remembered what trouble it had been before that, lighting oil lamps on dark winter mornings and dim afternoons or trying to milk the cows in the old stone and thatch byre by the shadowy lamp-light. That was all changed. In addition to the light they had the new cow-byre: cement-block, tin-roof, modern.

At nine o'clock the children met the Volkswagen van that served as a school-bus. At nine-thirty Mary put her head through the door between the kitchen and the bedroom and called Danny. She did the same at ten. Fifteen minutes later she reminded him that it was a mart day. Danny stirred, rolled over, stretched his legs and got out of bed.

After a breakfast of tea and bread and orange marmalade he went down to where he had left the dead rabbit. Bending over it he found the eye-balls gone, the eye-sockets small moist black holes, already tending to draw together and close. Untying the cord at the post end he carried the rabbit with him and hung it from a long rusty nail on a beam in a small tin-roofed shed. Returning to the house he said quietly, 'The grey crow lifted the poison.'

His wife looked up from the soda-bread dough she was kneading on the oil-cloth covered table. 'May save us some lambs this spring,' she said.

At 11.30 the cattle were still being driven into the welded-pipe pens but the air was already full of the sour smell of cattle slush. The penned animals stood restlessly, shifted nervously from time to time in wave-like movements that passed along their densely crowded swelling sides and backs from animal to animal. Men drove the cattle further into the pens, prodding, slapping, hitting, growling. The owner of the local insurance agency was among them, a slight looking man most days but then among the cattle in the pens in his shirt sleeves, his chest and stomach and muscular arms visible. He went over to a white-head bull, took hold of one of its long, sideways growing cream coloured horns, led it a foot forward. Young men in jackets and pants outgrown before outworn slid along the pipes prodding the cattle with their boots. The talk was of prices. Ireland was 'in Europe' but prices had fallen.

Inside the mart shed the cattle crossed the scale, went into the ring, were run about while the bidding started. Men slouched, grinned, frowned, stood straight, slumped on the wooden tiers, chatted intermittently, turned back again to watch the animals in the ring, pushed slowly through the crowded aisles. The droning amplified voice probed for starting bids.

'They're not so good'—the comment.

'Not so good now'—the reply.

The yellow-tan heifers crossed the scale into the ring. Danny listened for the starting price. 'Year-old Charolais,' the voice announced and searched for a bid, going lower, then lower again. Danny had decided to buy the new Charolais breed of cattle when they were introduced. The advice of the Dublin-bred agriculturalist, the assurance of his bank manager, the arguments of the government speakers, all had told him that cattle prices could not fall again 'when we go into Europe'.

'Charlies' (the agriculturalist had mastered the pronunciation but Danny had not) were what Europe wanted. They had the right conformation. The new names and new words themselves had an authority, an invitation.

Danny had studied the agriculture department's booklet carefully. The progressive farmer in the new Ireland, it said, no longer milked his two black cows in dung-splattered damp and dark stone byres but kept herds of modern breeds in modern cattle-sheds. 'Farmer Kelly' had taken an agricultural loan to expand his facilities and buy more cattle. A modern Artificial Insemination service put the highest quality prize bulls at his disposal without the necessity of keeping an expensive bull of his own. The increase of the herd had allowed him to repay half the loan the first year, the other half the second.

Danny had seen the opportunity, built the shed, bought the cattle. The first payment on the bank loan came due sooner than he expected. There had been many delays in putting up the shed after the materials were bought and paid for. The government grant to repay half the cost was late in coming. The bank payment was due. Finally a local politician had looked into it for him (it was just before an election) and the grant cheque had arrived. The payment was made.

It was discouraging how badly the cattle had done then. The 'Charlies' were soft, not like the old black cattle. They were harder to feed, needed more hay and of better quality. More grain. There was trouble with the 'bull'. It was hard to judge just when to call the AI. The AI men did not come on Sundays or holidays. They went on strike. Sometimes they came two days late. One of the cows had gone eighteen months without a calf.

In 1972 Danny and everyone had been convinced that cattle prices could only rise. In 1974 he saw that he had bought his new stock dear, spent more on them since, had no hope of a return.

Danny awoke from his thoughts just as the bidding ended

on the heifers in the ring. The final price was a third of what he had paid for his cows.

The insurance agent squeezed into a place beside him.

'Cattle not so good now, Danny,' he remarked.

'No, they're not.'

Silently they watched the animals enter and leave the ring. They followed the bidding, sitting quietly, intent on the efforts of the auctioneer to find a starting bid, an extra pound at the end. Danny's thoughts were on the bank loan. Selling his whole stock of cattle would not meet it. The manager had given him an extension. He had re-mortgaged, waiting for higher stock prices. Then prices had fallen again. The summer had been wet and cold, the grass short and thin on the meadows, the hay hard to win. The cost of buying it went to 75p a bale, then £1.25. A lot of the hay sold turned out to be mouldy.

'Everything you got to buy is dear, everything you got to sell is bad,' one of the men on the tiers complained in a high hoarse voice.

With the shortage of fodder and the great number of cattle in the country prices were bound to fall further. He did not know how he would meet the payments on his debt.

The insurance agent slapped his hands down on his knees and shrugged.

'S'pose there won't be much improvement on them today, Danny. Will you take a drink?'

At the hotel bar the two men stood and drank quietly. The rest of the bar was silent. Talk was difficult. The insurance agent brought up a subject that was troubling him: a missed life-insurance premium.

Danny took a small roll of pound notes from his pocket, peeled off seven of them and handed them over.

'Right, Danny. You're all right until spring.'

'I wish I was all right in more'n just that,' Danny answered. 'Spring be's a long way off.'

The agent looked at him. 'Oh aye, we're all in that boat,' he answered briskly. 'Too many cattle and not enough to give them.'

A solitary drinker turned to face them. 'Surely, that's it,' he said. 'We were all dying to get in, now we're dying to get out. But we can't. They have us snared.'

Danny looked up. As he put the roll of notes abstractedly back into his jacket pocket his hand found the small brown bottle.

'Maybe that's it,' he said and walked away from the bar drink in hand. The insurance agent left, the solitary man turned his back to the door.

A moment later Danny came out of the men's room in the hotel corridor, staggered slightly as he returned to the bar, put down his empty glass, hung his head heavily, had trouble breathing. Two farmers coming from the mart went up to him.

'You'll have another with us, Danny?' one of them said.

Danny looked at him blankly.

'You can manage one more, Danny,' the other added.

Danny slumped towards him. He was breathing heavily. They settled him into an arm-chair near the bar.

'He's had an awful lot since he left the mart,' the first said.

The barman came over and looked on curiously.

'He didn't have all that much now,' he said, raising his voice slightly at the end. 'Open his collar.'

They looked at Danny for a moment.

'I believe Dr Mullin would be at dinner at this hour next door. It might be wise to ask him to look at him. I can't leave the bar.'

The solitary drinker went out. In a moment the stout, ageing doctor came in, went over to Danny, bent over him, removed his tie, opened his shirt, examined his eyes, took his pulse, listened to his breathing.

'He has had a heart attack,' he said. 'We'll send for the ambulance at once.'

Duffy the pharmacist was a cattle-man himself. Farmers

often went to him for advice about sick animals in preference to the vet. He had heard that prices had slumped still lower but the long years of discipline when he had had to forego the marts and stay with his pharmacy, leaving only on selected days and hours when he himself had cattle in the ring, enabled him to put his mind on the prescription waiting to be filled and exclude everything else. He hardly noticed the girl shop-assistant's voice when she came in from her lunch and announced Danny Ward's heart attack.

Duffy went on filling prescriptions. After a while he heard the girl in the front part of the shop repeat the news about Danny Ward. He looked through the partition door.

'Which one is that, Sally?' he asked.

'Ward as keeps the herd of Charlies now,' she answered briefly.

Duffy returned to his prescriptions. He filled two more, then stopped. Going to his desk he took a ledger from one of the drawers and opened it in the middle. After a moment his eye found the entry he wanted: a date, then 'strychnine', then Danny's name. He picked up his phone and called the local sergeant. The sergeant promised to pass on the information to the hospital.

In the early afternoon the sergeant called Duffy. They had pumped the stomach but it was 'chancy would he make it.' He wondered how Mullin had diagnosed heart attack.

An hour later the insurance agent went into the North Sea Cafe and found Duffy at his afternoon tea. He sat down beside him and leaned over.

'Did Danny have poison bought?' he asked.

Duffy looked at the agent for a moment, his eyes reflecting. A slight movement of his head to the side revealed recognition of the question's purpose. Danny's debts were well known.

'He sometimes poisoned his land this time of year,' he answered.

'A bottle's been found in the men's room at the hotel,' the agent said.

A middle-aged woman, tall but slightly bent, came in to the cafe.

'They've called for Danny's wife,' she said to the girl at the cash desk, drawing her breath in. 'The priest has already been.'

The two women looked at each other, their eyes flat.

'How will she manage now?' the girl at the desk said after a pause.

The agent looked at Duffy again.

'It makes a difference of two thousand to us,' he said.

Duffy reflected. 'Oh, yes,' he said. 'The company won't pay.' After a moment he added, absent minded: ' **Danny's** debts.'

The Fence

Bobby McHugh was born in Brooklyn and came home to Ireland with an enthusiasm for everything Irish. He spent a few months with his uncle at the edge of Donegal Town and partook as deeply as he could of the Irish language, Irish music, Irish speech, Irish poetry and the Irish countryside, but above all of the Irish past. Then he and his wife bought a farm high in the hills. There Bobby hoped to find the old Ireland more fully preserved than anywhere else. He hoped to experience some last remaining drops of its essence. But he was also looking for something more universal, a return to nature, I think, and to what he called 'elemental human values'.

The farm had been occupied until a few years before and so needed only minor repairs. A single slate had slipped on the house roof and the byres all badly needed rethatching but otherwise everything was in acceptable condition. Bobby and Mary moved in and made the improvements needed for a minimum of modern convenience. Not modern by Brooklyn standards but modern for the hills of Donegal. They piped water down from a pure limestone spring that rose on the rock out-croppings behind the house and installed a glittering stainless steel sink and fixtures in the kitchen to receive it. A big white-enamelled iron range provided hot water for the taps and central heating for the rest of the house. A wind-charger gave them a useable kind of noiselessly generated electric current for their lights and for a few discreet kitchen machines.

Theirs was the only place for miles around that had electricity and on clear nights it stood out like a beacon among the soft glowing fuzz of the oil lamps of their nearest neighbours. It was an odd sensation to walk along through that remote, primitive region of Europe, in those hills where everything seemed scarcely starting to struggle out of the boundaries of the eighteenth century, much as in the annually late spring of the wet hill climate the grass and leaves and buds pushed their way only reluctantly and slowly forth from the cold ground, and to realize that within the still plain and humble exterior of the old, low crofter's house there had been gathered so much modernity as was represented even by Bobby and Mary's simple life.

Purists might have argued—as I was tempted to—that they had gone about their return to nature and to 'elemental human values' in the wrong way, that they had missed the point altogether, that they had imported the city into the country and so had carefully and all too effectively insulated themselves from the true experience waiting for them out there, the discovery of what life had really been like in pre-modern subsistence-farming days, when water was carried in by hand, and the only heat in the house was from the kitchen hearth, when the cooking was done in heavy soot-blackened pots over the smoky turf fire—so smoky that on sultry drizzly days the rooms filled with heavy white smoke and the consolation was heard from the old people that 'when the smoke goes through the house the warmth is going through it too'— when the only transportation apart from foot was by donkey or pony cart, and houses were built with hand-quarried stone, roofed with hand-cut timbers and thatched with hand-mown rushes, when a dozen children in a three-room house was commonplace and candles were a luxury (but no one knew how to read) and poetry did not arrive in books or little magazines but on the lips of auburn-haired raggedy men with slightly crooked eyes, and music was not an electronic sound from amplifiers and loud-speakers but was the singing and the dancing, the high voices and the rhythmic clap of farm boots on the clay floors of dim and smoky kitchens in time to the over-resined rasp of the local fiddle.

Maybe Bobby and Mary were right. It is not easy to experience the past as it really was. You can play at the past, you can act the role, but the past remains what it is: past. It will not revive for feeble modern imitations. To the men who actually lived it it was not, as it is to us, a rational alternative to an ominous, overcrowded, cancerous future. It was merely the present, the life they were born into and accepted. Indeed, they only partly accepted it. To them it was full of defects. They were always looking forward to the future. Bobby and Mary wanted the best of both worlds, the silence and purity of the country as it had been through so many centuries of civilized existence, with the comforts of the modern world.

Bobby's way of going about farming was interesting. He bought in something of everything. The sheep came with the land, were 'haunted' to it, as they say in Donegal, and would never wander off it even without fences, so he willingly paid a premium of an extra pound a head. They were known to be good breeding ewes anyway and were worth the price. He bought two milk cows and learned to milk, and two young calves to go with them, a donkey and cart he really had little use for (I remember him saying something about putting out 'top-dress'—the local term for manure—on the meadows, but in the end that job was done for him by tractors with automatic loaders and spreaders and the donkey merely got soft and fat and lazy and had more and more trouble even walking as his hooves grew out in long disabling arcs), and a large flock of laying hens, a huge speckled certified breeding rooster with a mighty voice that in a favourable wind was heard two miles down the valley, a dozen ducks, six turkeys, a goose and a gander. The farm was Bobby's modest approach to Noah's ark, as archaic and colourful from the outside as it was modern and neat and convenient within.

When Bobby and Mary had got that far all their neighbours, and all the local people for several parishes around, waited and watched to see how they would continue, how they would manage their land and their animals. Bobby bought a shelf of books on farming and husbandry, he paid frequent calls on the local agricultural adviser, a fiery-haired man from Dublin, and got the agricultural adviser to call on him and walk his farm and make recommendations for improvements and better farming policy. His neighbours had no comment, to him at least, on the agriculturalist but they knew too that there are styles in agriculture, as in everything else, and that 'scientific' findings (they never used the term themselves but only hinted at it vaguely) had a way of turning out wrong when applied to animals that had never themselves heard of those findings. The animals had traditions of their own, it seems, that were in their blood and so based on a longer experience and a longer unbroken series of experiments than any group of scientists could hope to achieve. For the old farmers every animal, every living individual, represented only the most recent link in an unbroken chain of individuals that stretched back to creation: and all those uncountable individual links in those limitless living chains had survived and even flourished without the intervention ever of agricultural advisers. They had only appeared on the scene half a human generation ago and changed their ideas and advice a dozen times or more since then. What Bobby needed, his neighbours thought, was more than the latest agricultural advice, more than his own city intellect, something beyond shrewdness, beyond instinct even. It was what they called 'luck'.

Bobby sensed his neighbours' reservations about modern methods and he was too much in love with everything traditional and Irish not to give at least as much weight to what they said as to his books on farming or the agriculturalist's recommendations. He spent long rainy afternoons and evenings sitting at hearths in low thatched houses listening to the old farmers talk about animals, drawing as they talked on lifetimes of experience and memory and even going, in their satisfaction at having found a fresh listener who had not already heard those same stories a dozen times over, back beyond their own lives to their fathers and grandfathers and recalling for Bobby's sake cows and ewes and sheep-collies and farmers and even places they themselves had never seen, but only heard of, sometimes at second or third hand. 'Oh aye! I often heard the old people say ...' was the phrase that marked those moments, or, 'You often hear tell of it.'

So Bobby tried to develop a mixture of approaches, to balance the modern ideas that he could not give up with the old ones that he was trying to accept, in so far as he could. The mixture did give him a kind of surprising luck. For Bobby took to his animals. In a way that no one had expected from a Brooklyn Irishman who had never owned more than a pet terrier he showed a real sympathy for his sheep and cattle and donkey and was out in all weather making sure that everything was all right. His college-educated brain accepted the fact that the animals too had brains. He laid it down as his basic principle that there was a reason for everything an animal did, even if he couldn't see it, and he quickly discovered that they do not always thrive from the effects of too much well-meant management.

He had a way of philosophising about nature that his neighbours must have found strange, if they heard it. Listening to him in his kitchen I felt his remarks were directed especially to me, another outsider, who could share his reactions to those experiences so new to us, so commonplace to everyone else in the hills. Though he had come to the hills with some thought in his mind of a 'return to nature' he was impressed as soon as he began keeping animals by the unnatural quality of what he was doing. As soon as he learned to milk he pointed out the 'cunning of man who shapes his hand into a ring to mock the sucking of the calf and steal the cow's milk.' He quickly saw that he was trying to crowd many more sheep on to his land than could exist there in any natural condition.

What he disliked most was having to dose them with chemicals that sometimes, when they went down the wrong way, choked the animal to death in seconds while farmers looked on helpless, or dipping them in the stinging phosphorus solutions that prostrated lambs and seemed, according to his neighbours, to grow less effective against insects every year. Most of the farmers near him, as he saw when they came to help him with the dipping, could not read the long paragraphs of tiny printed instructions on the green 5-gallon drums of concentrated poison and he knew that even those who could ignored them, pouring the oily brown liquid directly into the dipping bath from the drum without measurement until the mixture frothed and seethed, or, as they said, until it 'cut'. Measuring the remains of a new drum with a stick after his first experience of dipping sheep he found they had used three times the recommended concentration. Aside from the long-term effect on his sheep and himself, which he only guessed at, he saw at once how contrary he was going to the love of nature he professed when he fled the pollution of the city. Meaning to discharge the used dip into the neighbouring stream drop by drop over a period of days he had given way to the persuasions of his neighbours, who argued that the full bath was a hazard, 'lest a beast would get in it and drown,' but as the dip flowed out and mingled with and obscured the clear mountain water one of them had quickly remarked, 'That will give them eels in the lough a turn' and Bobby saw himself then creating, or spreading, the very evil he had so strongly condemned and fled from.

Another time when he had interfered with nature's course his reactions showed me just how far he was from being the country Irishman he would like to have been. Two large grey crows had been nesting near the top of a clump of tall sycamores in front of the crumbling deserted house on a derelict farm near Bobby's. The crows circled high above the ground in great reconnaissance flights that covered miles, swooping suddenly when they found any animal tumbled or sick or helpless for any reason and quickly pecking out its eyes. In the springtime the crows had a way of coming on ewes while they were lambing and pecking out the tongue of the lamb as it was coming from its mother's body, thus leaving it unable to suck, and so to live, or the ewe's eyes if she could not defend herself. Bobby watched the nest uneasily until, angry one day over the loss of a new-born lamb, he decided to destroy it. Fastening a series of sticks together until he had made a pole long enough to reach the nest he came over to my place to take me along—whether for assistance or moral support I was not sure—and prodded the nest, neatly woven of heavy sticks and shreds of sheep's wool, off the thin high branches it rested on. As it broke up and fell we saw and heard four young birds, each the size of a small hen and just covered with a down of grey feathers, drop to the ground. The big crows were not there, somewhat to Bobby's relief. I think he expected them to attack him in defence of the nest.

We walked back to his place and stood about waiting for their return. It was only a quarter of an hour before the large dark birds came flying up the valley from the south. As they reached the sycamores they converged, arching their wings and settling gently towards the nest. Finding it destroyed they rose instantly again into the sky with loud cries and shrieks, circling in ever-widening arcs, not together but separate, rising and falling in erratic and constantly varying patterns of flight in their wide search about the hills and fields and farms surrounding the clump of sycamores and the ruined house.

Bobby touched my arm and exclaimed, asking if I did not find 'something Homeric' about their wild cries and widening circles that carried them first high and far into the hills to the north, then down to the lake below and back again in vain search for their just-hatched progeny. We watched them in fascination as they flew about and searched and cried out in pain and anger, seeming at times threatening, then querulous, then inquiring, but never stopping their cries until finally they flew rapidly away to the south, down into the valley, and did not come back.

Was it because of his strangely ambiguous approach to farming and animal life, or in spite of it, that Bobby had such good luck with his animals in his first year of farming? At any rate it was not until his second season, when by the success of his first one he had increased the number of animals grazing his farm by fifty percent, that Bobby became aware that there was something basically wrong. There had been hints obliquely from some of his neighbours. They were too experienced to try to tell him anything he wasn't prepared to understand, but some had made suggestions.

'If you had a fence on the back of your hill between you and Gallagher there'd be no man going over your land,' one of them had said.

Bobby did not gather the import of the remark. Gallagher was a good farmer and a good neighbour. He often helped with the sheep. The first season he had been invaluable at the shearing when Bobby had hardly been able to shear a dozen of his own sheep in three days—an experience less tiring for him, he knew, in spite of his aching bones and muscles, than for the unfortunate sheep. It was from Gallagher he had learned much of what he knew about sheep. They had often talked about fencing and Gallagher had emphasized the sheep's love of freedom and of being able to wander.

'It's the ewe that travels as has the best lamb,' Gallagher would say.

'Oh aye,' someone else in the household would interject, 'the one that gets the change of grass will always do the best.'

'I hate to see a sheep in a fence,' someone else would add. 'Some way, they don't do.'

'No, they don't,' Gallagher himself would come in again. 'It bracks their heart—*it bracks their heart*.'

It was that phrase that stuck in Bobby's ears, possibly as much because of its quaintness as of any good sense that was in it. 'It *bracks* their heart.' Everyone had agreed that sheep like scope, they like to wander, and his own love of the un-broken countryside, the long view of hills, streams, distant mountains unmarred by any pole or wire, any reminder of man's unfeeling incursions on nature, those human reductions of what was essentially limitless and beyond mere ownership to something small, limited, possessed—that too made him dismiss the thought of a fence on the back of his hill before he had even considered whether there was an argument for one.

But Bobby had noticed that his sheep were not doing as well in his second year of ownership as they had done in his first. Some ewes died during the winter and some lambs died in the spring, so that though he had half again as many sheep as the first year he didn't have half again as many lambs in the second lambing season as in the first. And yet he had plenty of land for his flock, even at its increased size. The problem could not be lack of grazing.

It was because the sheep had done so well for him that he had not yet paid a lot of attention to their habits or to where they liked to graze. He let them follow their accustomed haunts. When his record of achievement slipped that second year he decided to observe them more carefully. Then he realized that his flock had tended to concentrate itself on the lowest part of his land, a soft marshy area of damp ground where, because it was more sheltered than the hill around it, the grass grew softer and faster. The sheep stayed down there, or rose only part of the way up the hill, ignoring the largest part of it and especially that part most prized by hill farmers and generally acknowledged to be the best for sheep, the 'wild hill' over the crest that sloped away towards the crooked mountain stream on the other side. In Bobby's case that was the largest part of the farm, long stretches of uninterrupted acreage covered with clumps of rough hill grass and green heather, indented with areas of perfect natural shelter where sheep could graze even in the strongest wind without, as the other farmers put it, 'feeling an air'. When he walked over that land he found sheep with an assortment of marks but never any with his own bright blue stripe of marking fluid over the middle of the back.

The only solution he could see was to 'haunt' his sheep to that part of the hill. In May the grass would be growing rapidly and sweet with continually fresh and tender shoots pushing above the ground, soft and attractive to the nursing ewes. Rounding up all his sheep with his border collie he slowly urged the reluctant flock up the hill. Their habitual grazing of the low wet ground had taken away a measure of their liveliness. It was hard forcing them to move against the hill. At the crest—and it took him more than an hour to reach it, so slowly did the sheep allow themselves to be pushed on—there was a region of eroded ground where the rain over many decades had eaten broad channels through the eight or ten feet of deep bog almost down to the rock below, leaving high round hillocks, small islands of heathery ground sticking out above the slippery mud.

It was a maze. 'The Mires' it was called locally. There the sheep could easily get out of his control and rush ahead of him and his dog as he drove them through one channel to double back through the next one. He found himself running awkwardly back and forth over the difficult ground—slippery in the channels, tiring going up and down over the hillocks—trying to keep the sheep together in a flock, arresting fugitives that slipped away towards the south and the low ground he had just brought them up from, then running back to keep the rest from scattering.

The mere problem of getting the sheep to the back of his hill, even before he could set about haunting them there, took a good bit of Bobby's time. He had been at the problem for a month before he finally got the sheep to rise up the hill and go through 'The Mires' to the other side. When he got them there he surveyed the area for the grassiest, most attractive piece of the ground, then herded the entire flock over to it and held them there for a while. They grazed avidly—it was certainly true that sheep like 'a change of grass'. When he had held his own sheep together for a while he went around all that part of his land rounding up his neighbour's sheep. At the beginning of the spring he had counted thirty or forty strange ewes grazing his land. By early June it was nearer to eighty. Rounding them all up now he put them back over the march.

Bobby kept this up all through the month of June, neglecting much of his other work. But his sheep seldom stayed long on the back of the hill, never longer than the following morning. Often he saw them hurrying back the same evening, returning quickly to the lowland grass they liked so well.

'You wouldn't think of a fence?' someone said.

'Along the top?'

'Aye. Or between you and your nearest neighbour?'

'But they don't go in that direction. They come back over the top.'

'Oh aye, you're right there. It's over the top they come.'

And the conversation stopped there.

It was only after a number of almost identical conversations that an old farmer, Gallagher's neighbour on the opposite side from Bobby, invaded Bobby's area of ignorance.

'If you had a fence between you and Gallagher there would be no man running over your land with his dogs, unsettling your sheep.'

Bobby suddenly remembered that the same old farmer had told him the same thing two years before when he had started farming. While the back of the hill was a piece of his own land he seldom saw, involving as it did a fifteen minute climb to reach it from his house, the old farmer who was advising him then lived on the slope that stood directly across the river from that hill, and so was able to see every sheep on it at every moment, and everything in fact that happened there.

'You mean he chases my sheep back over the hill?'

'He's got his own sheep to look after and round up, you know. S'pose your sheep wouldn't like the strange dog.'

Bobby decided he would have to fence.

That raised other problems. Where to put the fence was the first. Some advised him not to fence on the back of the hill at all but simply to run the fence along the road on the front slope of the hill—the dividing line between the low part of the farm and the high hill—and then put it part of the way up to the crest. That would discourage the sheep from going back to the low ground. Others insisted that a line of sheep-wire on the back of the hill only, between himself and Gallagher, would clear the ground for his own sheep. Neither solution seemed satisfactory. If he only fenced the march with Gallagher he would put the strange sheep off his land but nothing would keep his own from returning over the hill to the low ground they were used to, while if he only fenced the front Gallagher's sheep would still graze his land, and his own sheep could easily walk around the upper end of the fence, making that simple detour to get back to their preferred grazing. To do the job right, he decided—and he had discovered what a reluctance there was in the hills to do any job completely—he would have to fence across the front of the hill and all the way up over the crest and down to the river in the back.

'The hill will never be mine,' he told me, 'until it's properly fenced.'

That was when Bobby's problems really began. From the road in front to the river in back was just over a mile. I found him at his kitchen table one afternoon calculating the amount of materials. He would need 40 coils of sheep wire just for the single stretch from the road to the river, 14 more to go along the road on the front of the hill to meet the fences he had already put up around his inland meadow. It would take 18 large straining-posts to support the wire. He would need several thousand galvanized iron staples. The total cost of materials would come to about £260. He was not thinking about labour costs because he expected to do most of his work for himself or, following the custom of the hills, borrow a day's help from friendly neighbours when he needed it. Still, he knew there would be extras to pay for, as on any job.

Bobby decided to sit on the problem for a while and in the next months he made more attempts to persuade his flock to graze the hill, always without success. Fall was coming on, the days were getting short. He went on playing with the idea of the fence half-heartedly, as if he had no real intention of ever doing anything about it. His neighbours were amused by his perplexity. It became a useful recurring topic of conversation, interrupting the long silences on rainy nights around the hearths and kitchen ranges.

'Will he fence, do you think?'

'He'll hardly ever fence, I'm thinking.'

To which, after a long pause and a preparatory spitting of smoke-imbued saliva into the turf fire, someone would reply:

'He might yet.'

The different opinions represented different desires, for there were those who thought the fence undesirable, limiting the scope and free movement of their own sheep and their access to the high hills to the east, while others, even though their own personal advantage or disadvantage was not involved, were tired of seeing their neighbours make free use of land that was not theirs.

Then late one afternoon in September a lorry stopped in front of Bobby and Mary's house and dumped a large pile of reddish-coloured wood that turned out when sorted to be 700 larch fencing posts. A few days later a tractor arrived with sixty-two coils of three-foot sheep wire. The next day I saw Bobby with four fencing posts on his shoulder slowly climbing the hill. A few days after that I asked him how it was going. When he discovered just how long it took to carry four posts all the way to the river at the back—the first half of the trip uphill, the whole of it over rough, uneven ground—he decided to hire men to carry out the posts and coils of wire and went around from house to house making the arrangements. He found four men for the job but none of them ever came. He went around again and found four more and they didn't come either. It seems they were afraid they would lose their weekly government unemployment payments if they took any kind of job, even a temporary one.

That stopped Bobby again. The neatly stacked ruddy fencing posts and softly gleaming coils of wire lay like an inert reproach before his door, growing wet in the autumn rain. Then in the middle of October I found him with his donkey, its hooves freshly pared and iron-shod, an improvised pack-saddle tightly cinched to its back, twelve long fencing posts strapped to the saddle. They were making a slow progress against the hill. Impeded by his burden, the donkey refused to face directly into the slope, and Bobby had to lead him a long zig-zag course back and forth across the face of it ascending by gradual degrees. That increased the distance they actually walked from one mile to three or four—plus the mile back. Of course, the distances were getting shorter with each load but I noticed looking down from the crest of the hill that very few loads had actually been carried out.

There were other difficulties with the donkey. The pack-saddle kept slipping around and had to be re-tightened and it was hard to get the fence posts packed in and tied in such a way that they wouldn't jostle loose with the uneven jog and jump of the donkey against the hill. What finally persuaded Bobby to give up the donkey was a misjudged attempt to take a short cut through 'The Mires'. The donkey had shied back from the slippery ground but Bobby urged him on, seeing the flat grey slabs of stone showing through the surface of the soft brown bog and thinking they must provide a hard footing only an inch or two down. The donkey allowed himself to be coaxed on step by step for a few yards. Then, just when all seemed safe, his hooves broke the surface and his four legs plunged to the belly in the moist, sticky mire. Before Bobby could get the load of wood unstrapped the donkey began a series of violent heaves and lunges. The improvised saddle-girth snapped, the saddle fell away with the fence posts in a loose cluster on top of it and the donkey, quickly freeing his fore-legs, drew himself out of the mire and on to the solid height of the nearest heather-covered hillock. Then had come a full hour of mad gyration (Bobby told me about it later) when the donkey refused to leave his island of safety or risk another uncertain voyage on the brown sea of bog about him. His only response to Bobby's snapping of reins and clucking of tongue was to run in circles round and round the perimeter of the tiny hillock.

Bobby found himself looking around involuntarily every few minutes to see if anyone was observing. He knew his most dignified attitude would be to keep his attention solemnly fixed on the problem before him and not betray an awareness of his own folly, but he could not help looking up anxiously from time to time. There was no one in sight. After an hour of futile coaxing at the end of which he had only succeeded in getting the donkey to exchange one hillock for another and then return to the first, he stopped long enough to explore the ground for a possible route out. Then he saw he could make a kind of path with the eight fence posts and bits of loose flat stone and so he got the donkey home.

Bobby had been contemplating the idea of the fence for six months, another month had passed since the delivery of the materials, and he still had only managed to carry out a few dozen posts. The helpful neighbours who had advised him to fence had not taken that problem into account. They themselves were men who in their prime had carried hundreds of posts and scores of coils of wire out to remote borders of their land and not given the matter much thought. For them it had been easy to spend long days in heavy, steady physical work. The monotony of the work was probably largely assuaged by satisfying thoughts of confining their nearest neighbour to his own land and no longer having to see his infuriatingly large and well-fed animals poaching grass that didn't belong to them. Bobby was not their equal. He would have to find an easier way to do the work.

It was then that Mary thought of the dole office. If all those men were collecting unemployment payments from the government they must be available for work. The government, she decided, would be glad for a chance to get some of them off its books for a week. I listened to Bobby and Mary discuss that new idea for the better part of two hours one evening. They were enthusiastic about getting the fence finished by the middle of November when the ram would be put out to the ewes. The cost of labour would increase the price of the fence but at least it would get done.

On her weekly Friday shopping trip to town Mary stopped in at the dole office and told the man in charge she wanted four men to work at carrying out fence posts and coils of wire and that they would be paid 'the standard wage'. The man took a form from his desk and carefully filled in the information she gave him: employer, employer's address, type of employment, number of days employment, wages offered, and so on, and said he would send the men the following week. Mary assumed that meant Monday. When Monday came and no men appeared she couldn't be sure whether the man had specified a day or just said 'next week'.

The following Friday Mary went in and asked again about men for the work. It seemed there had been difficulties. There were no men available for the work. When she expressed her surprise at that, it was modified to *suitable* men. There was also the problem of transportation. But she had said she would pay the transportation if the men would come together in a taxi—it was ten shillings each way. He had not understood that, he replied, and was sure it would make a difference. The men came in on Tuesdays. He would send four of them out.

The next week was the first week in November and the days were getting short. The few days of dry weather the hill farmers look for at that time every year arrived, and they were busy trimming the excess wool from the bellies and sides of their sheep—neatening them up so that the sticky winter snow would not form into heavy, disabling balls of ice on the ragged ends of the fleece—clipping the wool off the tails of the ewes 'to make it easier for the ram', and giving the whole flock a final strong dose against stomach worms and liver fluke and a final dip in the purple-brown hand-stinging poison that killed every louse and tick and water- and snow-proofed the sheep during the wet winter to come. Bobby was as busy as the rest, exchanging days of labour at the neighbouring farms for help on his own. It did not surprise him no one showed up for work. He would not have been able to supervise them if they had come.

So the time for putting out the ram approached and no progress had been made on the fence. That Friday Mary was in the dole office again. This time the man merely shrugged in discouragement. If the men would not take the work he could not force them to.

So the fence had come to a stand-still before it had ever got started. The fence posts and the wire, no longer bright but turned a soft grey by the effects of air and weather, stood in undiminished stacks before the door. The sheep shunned the hill.

I waited to see how Bobby and Mary would face the situation then. They seemed to have forgotten the whole thing. Bobby was busy keeping his sheep rounded up and sorted into two groups for his two rams, one a traditional black-face with spiralling heavy horns, the other a hornless white-faced ram of a large breed never before used in the hills. The two rams, that would graze peacefully side by side at any other time of the year, had to be kept well separated then. No one was sure what would happen if they met. It was certain there would be a fight but no one knew whether the size and bulk of the white-face or the heavy horns of the black-face would have the advantage. Everyone thought it probable that one of them would be killed. Bobby kept them carefully separated, one in a closed field, the other on the hill, and he kept a close watch on them most of the day. Whichever one he had on the field would be put into a stone byre for the night. As for the fence, as nearly as anyone could see, that had been dropped for the winter at least.

But Bobby and Mary were still discussing the matter intermittently, working over in their minds the logic of the dole system. One night in their kitchen I listened to an eloquent dialogue on the peculiarities of a system that 'creates unemployment and retards economic development just where it is most needed'. Bobby went to see his local county councillor and explained that if he employed men who were on the dole that would not only relieve the burden on the treasury for a week, it would also increase the productivity of his farm and hence improve Ireland's trade. The councillor listened with his head down, looking at Bobby from time to time out of the sides of his eyes and biting his lip quickly. He promised to do what he could. He himself, he explained, needed men for some work on his own house and had a hard time getting any.

Bobby's annoyance at seeing his fence frustrated turned into an amusement, a major topic of conversation. He felt he was discovering yet another aspect of his ancestral homeland. He formulated laws relating chronic unemployment to chronic labour-shortage. He discoursed on the importance of joining the Common Market, which would put an end to the dole. Finally he asserted that he had always known what would happen if he tried to undertake any ambitious project requiring outside labour.

When he realized that all his talking was only a way of passing the time without getting anything done he prepared one more attack on the dole office. This time he inquired diligently beforehand about the official structure of the unemployment system, established the hierarchy of bureaus and officials he would have to write or visit in his fight, and began composing a series of letters meant for the provincial and national newspapers. He was thoroughly prepared for action when Mary stopped in at the dole office a fourth time one Friday in the middle of December.

The dole man listened to her request again. He may have sensed a certain new determination in her bearing or maybe he had got word from the county councillor that Bobby had been to see him. He looked slightly discouraged and explained that any men he might send would be useless for the work. Years on the dole had unfitted them to work for anyone. Mary persisted. The dole man went to his files and after some hesitation began compiling a list of men. After a quarter of an hour he stopped suddenly and got up to leave. Ushering Mary out he promised to mail her the list the next morning. She could choose the men she wanted and send it back to him.

To her surprise the list arrived in the mail a few days later. Bobby looked it over hastily. All the men on the list were well known to him. Most of them had agreed to come when he had approached them personally, then simply failed to appear. He suspected a trick. It was, somehow or other, just another means of delay. Without giving it any more thought he printed in large letters at the bottom of the list, 'SEND ALL AT ONCE', and sent it back the next afternoon with the mailman.

The following Monday was a day of heavy mist. Mary was feeding the hens when she saw a man coming along the road. It turned out to be one of the young men who had promised to come in the fall but had not. Bobby looked at him in puzzlement, almost having forgotten that he had asked for men to be sent.

'Do you want work?' he asked.

'I'm carded to you,' the other answered. 'I have to come to you.'

Bobby didn't stop to wonder about this new contradiction in the system but quickly put the man to work, even forgetting to settle on the wage beforehand. The first problem was to show him how to find his way out to the back in the thick winter mist. Though it was longer following the crooked march between himself and his neighbour's land, it was the only sure way. He led the way, himself carrying a load of slabs, and made sure his workman knew the route. By the time they got back to the house most of the morning had passed and Bobby remembered that he had not milked the cows or done any other work. As he started trying to catch up he also became aware that he had a cold coming on.

He told Mary to note down the times their solitary workman returned for a fresh load of posts. A mile out, a mile back: counting the hill climb and the burden he should be able to put out about seven or eight loads of posts—one round trip an hour.

The mist hung on the hill all day. Below the house they could see into the valley below and for miles beyond, while a hundred yards above the house was nothing but the white mist. Young Paddy appeared regularly just about when Bobby had calculated he should, rested briefly and then took up another load of posts. In the middle of the day he stopped for tea. He had brought his own tea and sugar, bread and butter and even his cup and only asked Mary for the boiling water. By the end of the short afternoon he had carried out seven loads of posts. That night Bobby calculated that even at the rate of eight loads a day it would take young Paddy eighteen days to carry out the posts. He could not imagine young Paddy doing eighteen days' work. Then there was the wire too.

The next day the mist had cleared but Paddy did not come back. Instead four other men arrived, in a group, on foot.

'Do you want work?' Bobby asked them.

'We're carded to you,' one of them answered, showing a yellow paper form. 'We have to come to you, if you want us.'

Bobby took a load of posts himself and led them up the hill, following the march even in the clear weather, thinking it a surer route in case the mist returned. About halfway along, near the crest of the hill, he found one of the loads of posts that Paddy had carried out the day before, then none at all until he came to the point near the river he himself had led Paddy to with the first load. As the men went back over the hill to collect their second load Bobby stopped near the crest to look around. Two hundred yards to the east he caught sight of four posts lying on a low hillock. Scouting around he found four more loads scattered about on the front of the hill.

'Paddy must have got lost in the mist,' the new workmen commented.

'But the march is easy to follow even in the mist,' Bobby reasoned.

'Sure, you wouldn't know,' one of them replied. Bobby noticed the easy-going lilt of his voice.

During the day each of the four men carried out seven loads, twenty-eight in all and Bobby climbed the hill from time to time to make sure they were going the right route. In the intervals he carried some of the scattered posts over to the march, his mind busy with rough calculations of how much work young Paddy had really done and how much it was really worth.

'Will you come back tomorrow?' Bobby asked as the men finished their late afternoon cup of tea and got ready to leave.

'We're carded to you,' they answered. 'We have to come to you if you want us.'

Then one of them added quickly, 'I have a cow her time is in tomorrow. She may be calving. You won't mind if I don't come?'

After the months of fruitless effort to get these same men to work Bobby was surprised at his new authority to insist on anything. He simply shrugged agreeably and tried not to express his pleasure at having made even a small amount of progress towards the fence.

The next day the mist had returned. In the early morning a light rain began to fall. Six men arrived, three of those from the previous day and three new men. The new men excused themselves for not coming sooner: some sheep had urgently needed dipping and dosing.

In the wet, cold mist Bobby led the six, each with a load of posts on his shoulder, along the march. Back at the house he felt the cold in his head turning into a painful roughness in his throat and chest and decided to spend the rest of the day in. The men were good workers, he could leave the carrying-out to them. He calculated that, with the forty or fifty loads they put out, half the posts would have been carried by that evening.

There was a dense mist again the next day. It was Thursday. Bobby was too sick with flu to go out. Nine men came—all those who had come before as well as two new ones. Bobby was puzzled by the irregular numbers but was happy at the thought of seeing the work done. Though he could not supervise them he had no intention of sending them away. It was a simple matter of carrying out fence posts and coils of wire: four posts made a load, or one coil of wire.

Mary thought it would be better if someone went out to keep an eye on the men, who had come in very irregularly the day before and were hard to keep track of. About ten a.m. she went up the road to the march and then started along it. She had been out about twenty minutes without finding anyone at all, or any sign of posts or wire, when she saw the white shape of a sheep emerge from the mist and come towards her. As she knew that ewes shun humans and always walk away from, not towards them, she sensed that something was different about this one. From the animal's large size she knew that it was a ram, and then she easily discerned the large horns and broad black face with the white star on the forehead.

She held her breath as the ram approached but she saw at once that he was more curious than anything else. She could see from his tentative step and the slight movement of his head from side to side as he sniffed the air and sized her up with alternate views of his round eyes that he was also puzzled by her. His heavy horns frightened her. She feared a hostile movement of his head. Her best course, she knew, was to stand perfectly still. The ram's curiosity was intense. He sniffed Mary's feet, her legs, the hem of her dress, stood back and looked her over again, then circled around her sniffing the air. It was evident that he had not previously encountered a being who belonged neither to the class of male sheep farmers he was used to nor to that of his ewes. Mary was somewhere in between. She on her part was wondering when one of the men would reappear along the march and lead the ram away. There was nothing she could do but remain perfectly still and not alarm the animal. Finally the ram turned and loped away down the hill, quickly enveloped in the mist. At that moment Mary heard the voices of the men somewhere between her and the house, conversing loudly as they went, though she could not see them.

Bobby decided he would have to get up, flu or no flu. In the afternoon he pulled himself out of bed, used a little of every patent medicine in the house, and went up the hill. To his surprise not nearly the right number of loads had been put out along the march. He had trouble finding any of the men. When he did they complained of getting lost in the mist.

'What about following the march?' he asked.

'But that's the long way,' they replied

He saw then that he would have to revise his system and he sent all the men home for that day, telling them to come back the first day the mist lifted. As it turned out, that finished the week because the mist continued through Friday. Saturday was a drier day and in the late morning the mist began to rise. Going around the hill Bobby found loads of posts and wire scattered about the land in no discernible order. Half the march had been supplied, about an equal number of posts had been dumped almost anywhere.

Bobby reviewed the situation. Nine men had come. There were three brothers who had fenced all their own land. Logically he should put them to work fencing and have the others carrying. He could not be sure that anything would get done unless he was out supervising even the simplest job.

The following Monday all the men came. He put the three brothers to work fencing and had the others continue the carrying. The fence started from the river. The first job was to carry out two of the heavy straining-posts. No one had thought of that before. Then there was the question of tools. Everything tended towards disorganization. Bobby saw that though the fence seemed like a plain line of wire when he was planning it, the completion of even that simple, two dimensional project required more planning than he had guessed.

He had put up a stretch of fence himself the year before and had drawn up a list of 'tools and materials for fencing'. Searching through his folder of farm receipts he found it. I saw it tacked inside the kitchen door:

TOOLS

1. Crow bar
2. Sledge hammer
3. Pliers
4. Nippers
5. Claw hammer
6. Rough saw
7. Plumb line
8. Hatchet
9. Wire-cutters
10. Goggles (for use with barbed wire)
11. Wire strainers
12. Spades
13. Scythe (for clearing rushes)
14. Scythe-stone
15. Bucket (for small tools)

MATERIALS

1. Straining-posts
2. Fence-posts
3. Props
4. Pegs
5. Sheep-wire
6. Bull-wire

7. Barbed-wire
8. Heavy staples
9. Light staples
10. Three-inch nails

Bobby was ready to go.

And from there on things went smoother. The three brothers, he found, could work without supervision. He soon learned to ignore them and found the fence going up in lengths of three or four coils—150 to 200 yards—at a stretch, perfect straight lines, the wire neatly strained against the heavy straining-posts, held rigid along its length by the evenly spaced upright fencing posts.

It was the other men that puzzled him. The carriers, later the helpers. No matter how he watched them they never seemed to get their simple jobs right. Reclaiming the scattered posts was the first task. Getting everything properly spread out along the march was the next. It was odd to him how little work he could get from those men even when he was standing looking on. There were areas where the ground had to be dug away in places, filled in in others, to bring it level with the bottom of the wire. If he set the men to do the work and left them, he found when he came back that nothing had been done. If he picked up a spade himself and went to work, it was as if his own will and muscles had to keep the rest of them at work. There was one young man, he noticed, who went through the motions of vigorous work but did very little, taking hold of a length of wire that was being strained between two of the heavy straining-posts and holding tightly to it as though it would fly away without his restraining grip, or jabbing a spade at the earth in a mimicry of vigorous effort, though the spade never pierced the ground. Then Bobby remembered hearing men say, 'Con will spare hisself.' But Con's brother after two years in a tuberculosis ward seemed to want to make up for his brother, driving himself instead.

I remember Bobby's lively description of his sensations on

the day the fence moved across the crest of his hill. A wind was blowing from the southwest, up from the sea ten miles below. There was a mist and spitting rain was falling diagonally across the hills. Used as he was to padding around those hills looking for his sheep in a silence broken only by the sound of the wind and the rain, the occasional bleat of one sheep calling to another, or the slap of his dog's paws against the areas of bare ground where the grass had not grown, he found it odd to hear the sound of men at work, the pounding of the sledge driving fence posts into the ground, the metallic knocking of the hammer against the staples as they clasped the wire tight against the wood, the loud talk of the men. As he moved across the crest of the hill that he was so used to seeing deserted, he found, accentuated by the cloud of mist that shut out all the surrounding world and added an intensity to the scene, a little world of active figures semi-enveloped in the fog that created an illusion of distance, depth, numbers. The enclosing, enveloping mist created an illusion of microcosm in Bobby's mind as he watched the work. His creative imagination came to life.

It was when the fence was almost finished and he could send most of his workmen away and keep only the three capable fencers, that he began to think about the way they had worked. The man in the dole office was right, he said, or mostly right. There were few men in the region suited for work. The dole had unfitted them for it. Then he stopped and wondered about those three who did work. They did not fit the pattern.

It was Bobby's first view of Ireland in an unsentimental light. I invited him to come down to Sweeney's pub one dry night and as we walked along the road he began to discourse on what he had learned about the people. He had always thought, he told me, that he was coming to live in the eighteenth century when he came to the hills. The stone houses, built up with clay for mortar, the roof beams and rafters rough-hewn from wood found preserved in the bog, the thatch of green rushes cut only minutes from the front door, all belonged to the pre-modern world. He had been amused watching his neighbours making the discoveries other farming communities had made in the eighteenth century or earlier: giving their cattle extra fodder in the winter along with the hay, experimenting with root crops, fencing their fields to control grazing. Gradually he had sensed that there was something older than the eighteenth century in the people around him. His conjecture went first to the Middle Ages. As the Renaissance had never penetrated Ireland (we both laughed as he said this) it was clear that basically Ireland was a medieval country.

His line of reasoning was so new to me that I was caught up by the idea at once and assented enthusiastically. But Bobby was quickly beyond me again. The Middle Ages had sent a feeble wash of spray across Ireland, he said, but that was all. It had left the outward form of a religion, and that deceived us. In actuality, he said, he knew at last that none of the great waves of civilization that had washed across Europe had ever reached 'this island beyond an island'. For that was the great fact of its history: it was 'an island beyond an island'—he had heard the phrase somewhere—and it lay at the north-westernmost edge of the great continent of human civilization.

Bobby, I could see, was giving himself distance from Ireland —that is, from the Ireland of his dreams, of his sentimental Irish-American past—and yet there was something very Irish about his discourse, with its vast romantic summations of history. From time to time the clouds broke and an intense star showed through. We were walking through an area near the bottom of the hills, where they met the flat land. The landscape about us as we walked was dimly illuminated by the cloud-diffused moon that highlighted the yellow rooves of the thatched cottages and the low grey mounds we knew were resting sheep. In the open view ahead there were no street lights, not even an electric light to be seen from any house window. In the grey harmonies of the soft hills and sloping fields there was something persuasive about Bobby's argument. The easy steady rhythm of our walking had a lulling effect that made it hard to think critically. I heard Bobby reciting the names of his neighbours for several miles around, a great catalogue of Gaelic names that somehow was meant to support his thesis. It was only the hypnotic quality of the landscape and of the night walk that kept me from seeing how strange Bobby's thesis was.

How had the successive eras of European civilization influenced these people? he asked. What characteristic of any great age had arrived here? The intellectual searching of the Greeks? The Roman genius for order? The Medieval capacity for suffering?

A group of sheep that had bedded for the night on the dry tar of the county road scurried into the darkness as we approached them. On a side road ahead of us we saw the light of a car coming and we hurried to catch the lift, if there were room. Like us, he was on his way to Sweeney's pub and we got in. The landscape disappeared and with it Bobby's strange oration, of which I had been the only audience. I listened to Bobby and the driver chatting in fixed, unvarying phrases about the weather—today's, yesterday's, tomorrow's. Nothing was visible except the intensely focused rapidly changing composition picked out by the headlights. I wondered how Bobby's discourse would have ended.

We had chosen a good night for Sweeney's pub, I thought. It was fairly crowded but no one was drunk. The only ones I knew were material for me to ponder in the light of Bobby's analysis: Sweeney himself—farmer, postmaster, shopkeeper, publican; a farmer turned merchant who drank only lemonade and drove an American car; two old cattle farmers past pension age; a hard-faced young man whose bad back provided an excuse for sitting all day and who liked to hint darkly at his membership in the IRA. Without difficulty of transition Bobby entered into the bar-room talk. His lofty generalizations were forgotten: local things were what he talked: illnesses, deaths, marts, prices, animals, charities, dance-bands, sports, racing, poker, darts. The merchant went to the dart-board, Bobby followed, Sweeney came from behind the bar to join them. There was a wood fire on the small hearth.

Even today a woman is a rarity in Sweeney's pub, and so when the married couple came in everyone looked in their direction. Bobby greeted them with a special enthusiasm. Like him they were Brooklyn-Irish and they were 'home' for Christmas. The man had been born in Donegal, his wife in America. Within a few minutes Bobby and the other two seemed to have resumed an old conversation, oblique references and brief remarks were quietly spoken back and forth, topics an outsider could not easily follow. The old farmers, the merchant, the younger men standing about looked on, waiting for their moment to get into it, to inquire in tentative voices about 'times away' and to gather opinions about current affairs 'at home'—the price of land, cattle, sheep, turkeys, the unrest in the North, the intentions of the English. There was a pause, glasses were refilled, the talk settled on Brooklyn. How were times? one of the old men wanted to know. He had worked there in the twenties. Times were good then. Plenty of money. The one thing he didn't like were the niggers.

A silence. A switch had been pushed. The American woman looked at the old farmer briefly, then away. She was ready for a different subject of conversation, but then someone in the crowd picked up the theme: the niggers had 'ruined all in the States'.

I saw Bobby looking at me as though wondering whether I was following the conversation with a correct understanding of the context.

'How do you define a nigger?' the American woman asked softly.

There was an uneasy sense of challenge and the lemonade-drinking farmer-merchant cleared his throat quickly.

'I suppose that's a word not used much any more,' he interposed.

I saw Bobby still looking at me, and I could see his eyes communicating something about all that he had said on our walk down and before that all through the winter when he had been preoccupied with the problem of getting his fence put up. His expression was no longer the soft, diffused expression of one more Irishman among many, but that of the strange intellectual pondering his long generalizations and historical syntheses, relating the small everyday events of this tiny island to the long movements of a continent's history.

His look alerted me to watch out then and see his generalizations coming to life. The American woman was once more about to drop the subject. She had turned to her husband and was going to suggest—it was easy to tell—that they leave, when one of the younger men resumed:

'Call them what you want, it's the niggers that ruins all in the States.'

The merchant evidently felt it was not too late to divert the tendency of the remark.

'You've worked with the *negroes*, I suppose,' he said, 'in the States. You would know them better than us.'

The American woman was silent for a moment. When she began to talk it was odd how her voice took on a very slight Donegal intonation that I had not noticed before.

'We have plenty of blacks over there,' she said softly, 'but it appears to me that the niggers are over here.'

Bobby smiled slightly, head down. He had caught the gist of her little bit of rhetoric at once. No one else had, however. There was a puzzled silence. Probably she would have pursued the subject, but the merchant quickly raised the question of the annual subsidies on sheep and cattle, how high they would be, or if they would be given at all, decisions eagerly awaited every year by the drinkers in Sweeney's pub.

Rounds of drinks were called for. It was getting late. Having had enough of the stuffy atmosphere of the crowded room I left shortly afterwards. When I saw Bobby a week or so later he told me about the 'splendid scene' that had followed. The talk had eventually gone back to the inevitable question of the North and getting the English out, and then to the usual themes of Irish politics: exploitation by foreigners, corruption, graft, the dole: and then back to the 'niggers'. Then the American woman had spoken her piece at last, told them that the blacks in America had discovered the task of changing themselves, but in Donegal men lay in bed until noon, rising early only on the day they went to get the little handful of government dole money and the small bag of sugar and the half pound of butter that went with it, finishing the morning in the pub, then home drunk, to bed again. Bobby laughed at the way she had turned the word 'nigger' back on the loungers in the bar. Their faces had grown long but no one answered. After she left there was a silence and someone had finally commented:

'There would be no man fit to live, only for the dole.'

The fence that had been going so smoothly hit a snag only half a day's work from the end. Bobby's three good workers suddenly announced that they had too much work of their own to do any more for him just then. They didn't know when they would get back. Bobby realized with astonishment that the strange magic that had brought so many men to work had suddenly evaporated. He looked at the fence that had come more than a mile from its start on the back of the hill to stall then, totally useless, like a chain that lacks its final link, only yards from the goal. Then surprisingly Gallagher himself came over to see how things were going and offered to lend a hand, and he and Bobby finished the work together.

Looking across from my own place a mile away I knew the fence was finished when I saw Bobby round up his sheep from the low wet ground they so preferred and herd them through the new gate on to the dry sloping hill above.

It was the middle of January. I was leaving for two months and did not see Bobby again that winter. From time to time I wondered how the fence had worked out, whether he felt it was worth the time, effort and money that had gone into it.

I knew how unpredictable animals can be, like all living things, and how often they responded negatively to man's most positive intentions. When I got home in mid-March I asked Bobby about it.

He smiled recollecting the work on the fence. His first reaction to the new fence had been one of personal disappointment at the change he had brought about in his own landscape. He had even felt sorry for Gallagher's sheep when he saw them standing and looking wistfully through the wire lattice, as through prison bars, at the ground they had so contentedly grazed a short while before. Seeing the long straight line of wire and posts from a mile away he had perceived it as a scar on the hills, an ugly symbol of division between neighbour and neighbour, even of the very struggle for acquisition and power that he had tried to escape when he came to live in the hills. The fence spoke to him of the control of living things, confining, forcing them into unnatural channels, like the dull straight narrow streets of the modern city he had left. It became a part of the same human ingenuity by which men shaped their fingers into cunning loops to steal the cow's milk. He remembered too how looking at the new fence he had involuntarily thought of the hundreds of yards of rusted-out wire he himself had removed from his farm when he bought it, and the way lengths of it caught in the fleece of the sheep or around the legs of the cattle, tearing their flesh or even immobilizing them, leaving them helpless until someone found them. In a short while, ten or fifteen years, this fence too would become a torn, rusted-out hazard to animals. In that way the fence became to him a symbol of transience, of the passage of time, of decay, of the temporary nature of all human effort.

All these thoughts were forgotten when Bobby put the fence into use. The sheep had congregated near the bottom for a few days and he made no attempt to drive them up. Gradually they had risen up the hill themselves. On the back of the hill and to the east they were free to wander around and down again along the derelict farm beside Bobby's and he waited to see if they would descend. Instead, as he had hoped, they had found their way ever higher into the rough unoccupied hills near Blue Stack, high, dry, lightly grazed land covered with a heavy coarse grass. There Bobby's sheep had flourished and he had only herded them to his lowland fields a few days before they were due to lamb. The fence had been a success.

I knew that Bobby had forgotten his reflections on the 'island beyond an island' that had never experienced any of the great movements of civilization. It seemed pointless now, ten weeks later, to ask him to finish that odd oration he had started on the walk down to the pub that winter night. It was late and I was ready to leave when I mentioned it to him tentatively.

For a moment Bobby did not recognize the subject I had raised. Then gradually he recalled the ideas and how he had expounded them. He had lost interest in them, it was clear, reconciled as he was to the peculiar difficulties of living in the hills by the success of the fence and the good condition of his animals. Then he took up the theme again, as though growing interested in someone else's words and ideas. It was true, he said. It was what fascinated him about the hills. Here in the remote northwesternmost hills of the island beyond an island Europe was scarcely felt, even today. The great movements of civilization, its great achievements and deadly wars alike, from ancient times even until today, had only been (I remember the phrase) 'the unwelcome echoes of a distant unrest.'